Interactive Mathematics Program®

Integrated High School Mathematics

I M P

YEAR 3

Calculator Guide for the TI-81, TI-82, and TI-83

Includes Blackline Masters

Brian Lawler

KEY CURRICULUM PRESS
Innovators in Mathematics Education

About Brian Lawler

Brian Lawler has taught each of the four years of the Interactive Mathematics Program and served as a technology specialist at Eaglecrest High School in Aurora, Colorado. He has led teacher inservices for the Rocky Mountain Region of IMP and has participated as a teacher reviewer of the curriculum for Key Curriculum Press.

This material is based upon work from the field test version of IMP Year 3 student materials supported by the National Science Foundation under award number ESI-9255262. Any opinions, findings, and conclusions or recommendations expressed in this publication are those of the authors and do not necessarily reflect the views of the National Science Foundation.

Interactive Mathematics Program® is a registered trademark of Key Curriculum Press. IMP and the IMP logo are trademarks of Key Curriculum Press.

Key Curriculum Press
1150 65th Street
Emeryville, California 94608
510-548-2304
editorial@keypress.com
http://www.keypress.com

10 9 8 7 6 5 4 3 2 1   02 01 00 99 98
ISBN 1-55953-352-8
Printed in the United States of America.

Consultant
Dan Fendel

Editor
Mary Jo Cittadino

Senior Editorial Assistant
Jeff Gammon

Reviewers
Mike Bryant
Kathy Sanders

Production Editor
Jason Luz

Production Manager
Diana Jean Parks

Cover Design
Terry Lockman
Lumina Designworks

Interior Design
Kristen Garneau
Garneau Design

Publisher
Steven Rasmussen

Editorial Director
John Bergez

Contents

Introduction to the Year 3 Calculator Guide

Graphing calculators are inexpensive yet immensely powerful tools that allow students to explore and grasp mathematical concepts. Calculators can give immediate feedback as students conjecture and test their conjectures. They can run a repetitive computation in a matter of moments and display results in several forms. They allow students to become excited about what they can do with mathematics.

As students master basic mathematical ideas through these modern tools, they quickly move on to more sophisticated mathematical applications, problems, and understanding. High-end topics that had not previously been accessible to high school students now are. Students can easily explore real-world situations, where the numbers are not always simple integers.

The Interactive Mathematics Program's curriculum is designed for a modern mathematics classroom where students are equipped with graphing calculators. This guide facilitates the use of the Texas Instruments graphing calculator in connection with Year 3 of the IMP curriculum.

How Does the Calculator Guide Work?

The guide begins with a brief introduction to the Texas Instruments graphing calculator and then follows the IMP Year 3 lesson plans through the units: *Fireworks, Orchard Hideout,*

Meadows or Malls?, *Small World, Isn't It?*, and *Pennant Fever*. This guide provides technical information when an activity requires calculator use. For other activities, the guide contains ideas about how to use the calculator as a natural tool within the context of the problem or as an enrichment or extension of the activity. The guide also provides hints or suggestions for avoiding possible pitfalls while using graphing calculators. Screen shots are of the TI-83 unless otherwise noted. In most situations, the TI-82 and TI-81 screens will be very similar.

Which Calculators Can I Use with the Calculator Guide?

The guide is written to meet the needs of IMP Year 3 teachers and students using a TI-81, TI-82, or TI-83 graphing calculator. If you are using the TI-80, follow instructions for the TI-82 and TI-83. If you are using a TI-85, TI-86, or TI-92, you can perform all the functions and operations described in this text, although the key sequencing and/or specific language structure may differ. If the necessary adjustments are not readily apparent, consult the Texas Instruments Guidebook.

Although this guide does not address the specifics related to other brands of graphing calculators or computer software, the same mathematical principles underlie each tool. Adjustments for keystroke and language are the only modifications needed to use these other tools.

Keep in mind that the TI-82 and TI-83 (as well as the TI-85, TI-86, and TI-92) have sufficient capabilities for all four years of IMP, but the TI-80 and TI-81 do not.

TI Calculator Basics

This section of the guide describes how to use some basic features of the graphing calculator. These are general instructions on operating the graphing calculator. Other chapters in this guide give instructions on operating the graphing calculator that are directly related to meeting the needs of the specific IMP curriculum units.

Using the Keypad

Many of the keys on the TI calculator have two other functions in addition to the primary function written on the key itself. The secondary function appears in small letters above the key to the left. The ALPHA function appears above the key on the right. Note that for the TI-83, the functions above the keys are color-coded to the 2nd and ALPHA keys in the upper left region of the keypad. In addition, many operations can be found in various menus or in the [CATALOG] on the TI-83.

Using the 2nd Key

```
√5
        2.236067977
```

The secondary function often performs an operation that is the inverse, or opposite, of the primary function on the key itself. For example, the x^2 key has the square-root function as its secondary function, because squaring and finding the square root often work as inverses. Notice that the ON key has OFF as its secondary function.

To indicate a secondary function, this calculator guide uses the symbol 2nd and then shows the function itself in brackets. For example, 2nd [√] indicates the square-root function above the x^2 key.

```
√(5)
        2.236067977
■
```

Note that the TI-83 automatically inserts an open parenthesis after the √, as it does with many other functions. This may help you to use order of operations properly in complex calculations. Now try it yourself. Use the 2nd [√] key sequence to find the square root of 1998. Then check your answer with the x^2 key.

Use the 2nd key followed by either the up or down arrow key to adjust the screen's contrast. To adjust the screen by more than one step at a time, press the 2nd key and then hold down the up or down arrow key. When the level indicator in the upper right says 8 or 9, you will need to replace your batteries soon.

CALCULATOR INSTRUCTIONS

Using the ALPHA and [A-LOCK] Keys

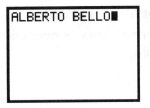

The ALPHA key gives the ALPHA function, which allows you to use the letters above the keys on the right. Most of these are letters of the alphabet. For example, pressing ALPHA A produces the letter A on your screen.

The ALPHA key only affects the very next key you press. Press 2nd [A-LOCK] to lock your calculator into ALPHA mode. Your calculator will stay in that mode until you either press ALPHA again or change screens. Practice by writing your name on the calculator screen.

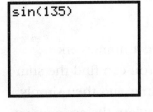

Do not use the ALPHA mode to spell out another command, such as sine. The calculator understands the command only when it is entered by pressing the SIN key.

Returning to the Home Screen

There are several different displays, or screens, on your TI calculator. The main screen is called the home screen. This is where you will do most of your calculations and run programs. If you find yourself at another screen, you can return to the home screen by pressing 2nd [QUIT].

Editing What You Type

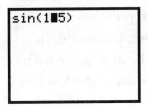

To clear your screen, press CLEAR. If you are entering a calculation, press CLEAR to clear the line and then press it again to clear the screen.

Enter a calculation like the one shown here, but don't press ENTER yet. You can use this calculation to practice your editing.

To replace a character or command, use the arrow keys to place the cursor over the character or command you wish to replace. Then type the new character.

To delete an entry, place the cursor over the entry you wish to delete and press DEL.

Continued on next page

```
6*_in(145)
```

To insert a character or command, place the cursor at the spot where you plan to insert and press [2nd] [INS]. (On the TI-81, [INS] has its own key.) Then key in what you want to insert. Press [ENTER] to execute the command, or use the arrow keys as needed to make additional entries or to do futher editing.

Recalling a Previous Entry

```
1+sin(√(5/6π))
        1.028236051
1+sin(√(5/6π))■
```

To recall a previous entry, press [2nd] [ENTRY]. This will repeat the last entry you keyed in onto your screen. If you press [2nd] [ENTRY] repeatedly, you will move back through previous entries one line at a time, so you can actually recover something that you did several steps earlier and that has scrolled off the screen. (The TI-81 can recall only the most recent entry.)

Working with Exponents

```
2^8
              256
■
```

The TI calculator uses the ^ symbol to indicate an exponent. For example, use the keystrokes [2] [^] [8] to calculate 2^8.

We raise numbers to the power 2 often enough that the calculator provides the $\boxed{x^2}$ key for this purpose. Calculate 99^2.

Using the Previous Answer

Sometimes you want to perform a sequence of calculations in which each answer builds on the previous one. (Some calculators have a "memory" key that helps you do this.)

```
9+9+7+10+4
               39
Ans/5
              7.8
Ans*10
               78
■
```

For instance, suppose you want to determine a homework percentage after five 10-point assignments. You can find the sum of the scores as in the first line of this example, and then simply press [÷] [5] to complete the next line to calculate the assignment average. The calculator automatically uses the previous answer, represented as **Ans**, to continue its calculations. Because each assignment is worth ten points, multiplying the average score by 10 yields the average percentage score, as shown in the last line of the screen.

CALCULATOR INSTRUCTIONS

Using the MODE Key

Press MODE. This key gives you the option of controlling certain aspects of how the calculator displays and interprets information.

(The screen shown here is a TI-83 screen. Other calculators have slightly different MODE options, so their screens will look different.)

To change options, move the cursor to the option you want using the arrow keys, and press ENTER.

The first two lines of the display control the way numbers are displayed on the home screen. On the first line, typically, **Normal** is appropriate. The **Sci** option refers to scientific notation, which you or some students may prefer. (*Note:* If the calculator displays a very large or very small number, it will use scientific notation even if you selected **Normal** in the MODE screen.) The **Eng** option refers to engineering notation, which is a variation of scientific notation.

The second line allows you to tell the calculator how many decimal places to display. **Float** is a useful option because the calculator will display up to ten digits, as well as a negative sign and decimal point (if needed).

The third line refers to units for angle measurement. The IMP curriculum does not introduce the use of use radians for angle measurement until Year 4. You need to be aware, however, that the calculator will default to the radian mode whenever the calculator memory is reset. It is always a good idea to check this option when you are using trigonometric functions such as sine or tangent.

Some of the other standard MODE settings are **Func** (or **Function** on the TI-81), **Connected**, and **Sequential**. Highlight these if you have not already done so. Investigate the other options on your own. The setting **G-T** (found only on the TI-83) creates a split-screen display of both a graph and a table, and is a favorite of students when they are investigating functions.

CALCULATOR INSTRUCTIONS

Function Graphing

These instructions describe the five basic graphing keys. You will find these keys immediately below the calculator's screen.

Using the [Y=] Editor

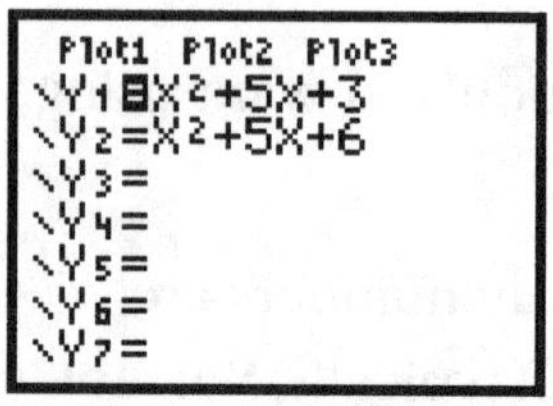

```
Plot1 Plot2 Plot3
\Y1◼X²+5X+3
\Y2=X²+5X+6
\Y3=
\Y4=
\Y5=
\Y6=
\Y7=
```

Press [Y=] to display this screen and enter functions. Use the [X,T,θ,n] key for the independent variable X when you enter a function. (This key looks different on different calculators; look for a key with an X and a T on it.)

To remove a function from this list, move the cursor to that line (to the right of the = sign) and press [CLEAR].

You can also make a function inactive without removing it. To do this, move the cursor over the = sign for that line and press [ENTER]. The = sign will no longer be highlighted. In the example shown here, the function $Y_1=X^2+5X+3$ is active and the function $Y_2=X^2+5X+6$ is inactive. The calculator will graph only active functions. To make the function active again, move the cursor to the = sign and press [ENTER] again.

Setting the Viewing Window

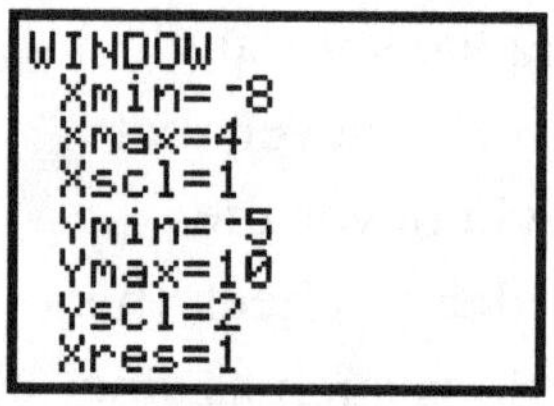

```
WINDOW
 Xmin=-8
 Xmax=4
 Xscl=1
 Ymin=-5
 Ymax=10
 Yscl=2
 Xres=1
```

Press [WINDOW]. (On the TI-81, this key is labeled [RANGE].) This is where you tell the calculator what part of the graph to show and how to scale the axes. The **Xmin** and **Xmax** values determine the left and right bounds of the graph. The **Ymin** and **Ymax** values determine the bottom and top bounds. The **Xscl** and **Yscl** values determine the frequency of the tick marks on each axis. If your calculator has another value, **Xres**, it should be set at 1.

Continued on next page

CALCULATOR INSTRUCTIONS

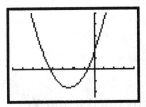

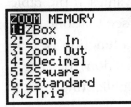

Displaying a Graph

Press GRAPH. This tells the calculator to draw the graphs of the active functions in the Y= edit screen. The portion of the graph you see will match the settings in the WINDOW display.

Exploring Graphs with ZOOM

Press ZOOM. The ZOOM features are another way to tell the calculator what part of the graph to show, and they automatically adjust the window settings. Each feature has its own purpose. **ZStandard** (or simply **Standard** on the TI-81) is handy because it resets the window to a standard setting. To use **Zoom In** or **Zoom Out**, highlight your choice and press ENTER. A blinking cursor will appear on the graph. Move the cursor to the spot you want to zoom in to (or out from) and press ENTER again. **ZSquare** adjusts your window to keep your graphs from being stretched or distorted.

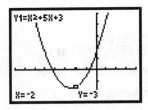

Exploring Graphs with TRACE

Once you have a graph displayed, press TRACE and experiment with the left and right arrow keys. Observe at the bottom of the screen the *x*- and *y*-coordinates of the cursor. Use **Zoom In** or **Zoom Out** in conjunction with the TRACE screen to adjust the trace results. If you have graphed more than one function, use the up and down arrow keys to move the cursor between the different functions.

CALCULATOR INSTRUCTIONS

Function Tables

(The TI-81 does not have the TABLE feature.)

Displaying a Table

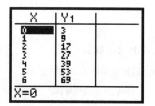

Press [2nd] [TABLE]. The table will display columns titled **X** and **Y₁**, although the columns may or may not display values. If the table doesn't have values in both columns, check to see that one (or more) functions are active in the [Y=] screen. If a function is active, check the [TBLSET] screen (see the next section). Be sure **Auto** is selected for **Indpnt:** and **Depend:** by highlighting and pressing [ENTER].

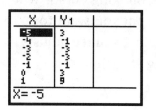

Once the table is displayed, use the arrow keys to move around in and to scroll the table. If you want to see values prior to the first row visible in the table, place the cursor in the **X** column of the values and scroll up to move backwards through the table. The screens illustrate how one student explored the function **Y₁=X²+5X+3**, given in *The Ups and Downs of Quadratics.*

Adjusting the Table

To make adjustments to the table, press [2nd] [TBLSET]. **TblStart** (or **TblMin** on the TI-82) determines the *x*-value at which the table will begin. **ΔTbl** determines the increment between any pair of consecutive *x*-values in the table. You can "zoom" in on the table by adjusting these values. Investigate the effects on the table by changing the **Auto** and **Ask** options.

CALCULATOR INSTRUCTIONS

Plotting Points

The graphing calculator will plot lists of data pairs in its function graphing screen for uses such as prediction or curve fitting.

Entering Data Pairs

Before you can plot data sets, you must tell the calculator what you wish to plot. To enter data sets on the TI-82 or TI-83, first press [STAT], and then choose the already highlighted **1: Edit...** by pressing [ENTER] to get to your screen of lists. Enter the data set like an In-Out table in lists **L1** and **L2**. (You can use any of the lists, or you can name your own on the TI-83.) If either list already contains data, a shortcut to clear the list is to put the cursor on the list name at the top and press [CLEAR] [ENTER].

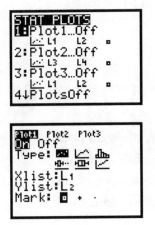

The example here shows the population data set from the central problem of *Small World, Isn't It?* Notice that the display uses scientific notation for large numbers.

(To enter data sets on the TI-81, press [2nd] [STAT]. Then, press the right arrow key to select the **DATA** menu, press the down arrow key to highlight **ClrStat**, and press [ENTER] twice to clear any data already in the list. Return to the **Data** menu and select **1:Edit**. Enter the data set as ordered pairs.)

Setting the Plot Editor

To set up the TI-82 or TI-83 to graph your data set, press [2nd] [STAT PLOT]. You should get a screen like the one shown here. (There is no plot editor on the TI-81. Go directly to the section *Setting the Viewing Window*.)

Select the Plot 1 editor to set up the calculator for your data set by pressing [ENTER] to display the Stat Plot editor for Plot 1. Match the screen shown here by highlighting and pressing [ENTER] on each of the options. Press [2nd] [L1] and [2nd] [L2] to enter them at **Xlist** and **Ylist**. Choose any **Mark** you like.

Continued on next page

Before you graph your data set, check a few things. First, go back to [2nd] [STAT PLOT] and make sure Plot 2 and Plot 3 are turned off. To turn off plots, move the cursor to highlight Plot 2. Press [ENTER]. Move the cursor to highlight **Off** and press [ENTER]. Repeat these steps to turn off Plot 3. To turn off all plots, go to [2nd] [STAT PLOT], highlight **4:Plots Off**, and press [ENTER]. Also, press [Y=] and make sure all functions are deleted or turned off.

Setting the Viewing Window

Before you do any graphing, you must set the range for the calculator's viewing window. Press [WINDOW]. (On the TI-81, press [RANGE].) The screen shown here displays one reasonable window for the *Small World, Isn't It?* data set.

This window is set up so that **Xscl** asks the calculator to show a tick mark for every 50 units on the *x*-axis. **Yscl** instructs it to show a tick mark for every 500 million people on the *y*-axis. You can enter very large numbers like these using the scientific notation feature of the calculator. For example, instead of entering **6000000000**, simply press [6] [2nd] [EE] [9]. (On the TI-81, press [6] [EE] [9].)

On the TI-83 and TI-81, use **Xres** = 1. This is not an option on the TI-82.

An alternative method for setting the window range quickly for plotting data on the TI-82 and TI-83 can be found in the **ZOOM** menu. Press [ZOOM], highlight **9:ZoomStat**, and press [ENTER].

Plotting the Data

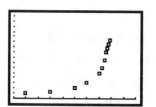

To view the plotted points at any time, simply press [GRAPH]. It's as easy as that!

(On the TI-81, pressing [GRAPH] will not graph the data points. You'll need to press [2nd] [STAT] and select the **DRAW** menu. Highlight **2:Scatter** and press [ENTER]. The Scatter command should appear on the home screen. Press [ENTER] again to view the scatter plot.)

Continued on next page

CALCULATOR INSTRUCTIONS

Displaying a Function and the Data Set

To display both a function and the data set on the TI-82 or TI-83, enter the equation in the [Y=] edit screen and then press [GRAPH]. If the equation does not match the data well, it may not show on the screen.

(If you press [GRAPH] on the TI-81 after changing features of the graph, the calculator will graph any [Y=] functions, but your data set will not appear. You'll need to give the **Scatter** command again.)

CALCULATOR INSTRUCTIONS

Programming the Calculator

The steps given here outline how to create and run a program. Recall there is never a need to tell the calculator to "save."

Creating a New Program

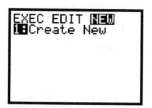

Press ⌜PRGM⌝, highlight **NEW**, and press ⌜ENTER⌝. (The TI-81 does not have a **NEW** menu. Instead, go to the **EDIT** menu, place your cursor at the first available unused program, and press ⌜ENTER⌝.) Key in a name for your program and press ⌜ENTER⌝. (On the TI-81, key in the name of the program on the first line of the screen.) The ⌜PRGM⌝ editor will be displayed. This is the screen where you actually write the program. Each colon is a new command line.

Running the Program

To run your program, return to the home screen by pressing ⌜2nd⌝ [QUIT]. Press ⌜PRGM⌝. You will see that **EXEC** (which means "execute") is already highlighted. Highlight the program you want to run and press ⌜ENTER⌝. The title of the program you selected will appear on the home screen. Press ⌜ENTER⌝ once again to run the program.

Breaking a Program

To interrupt or stop a program once you have begun running it, press ⌜ON⌝. The **ERR:BREAK** menu is displayed. You can select either of the two options: **Goto** will return you to the line of instruction in the program where the interruption occurred; **Quit** will return you to the home screen.

Continued on next page

CALCULATOR INSTRUCTIONS

Editing a Program

To make changes to any program in memory, press PRGM ,
highlight **EDIT**, use the arrow keys to highlight the program
name, and press ENTER . Use the arrow keys to move around
within the program command lines. On the TI-83 only, pressing
ALPHA and then an up or down arrow key functions like a
page-up or page-down command. You can delete, overwrite,
or insert. Press CLEAR to clear all program commands on the
command line (the colon remains).

Resetting Calculator Memory

The TI graphing calculator allows you to manage its allocation of memory in the **MEMORY** menu. This can be useful when you are working with large programs or matrices and the calculator runs short on memory. It is also a useful way to reset variables, lists, and matrices.

Clearing All Memory

You can reset the memory on your calculator, restoring it to the factory settings. Press [2nd] [MEM] to display the **MEMORY** menu. (On the TI-81, press [2nd] [RESET].) Highlight **Reset** and press [ENTER]. (On the TI-83, select **1:All Memory** and press [ENTER].)

The calculator gives you one more opportunity to reconsider. By selecting **2:Reset**, you will restore memory to factory settings, reset system variables to default settings, and delete all nonsystem variables, data sets, and programs. If the screen is faded or blank due to low batteries, adjust the screen contrast. To do this, press [2nd] and then press and hold the up arrow key until the contrast is satisfactory. Also, the calculator will be reset to radian mode. Press the [MODE] key to change the unit for angle measurement to **Degree**.

Deleting Specific Items

To increase available memory or to reset certain variables, you can simply delete specific types of data from the calculator's memory. (This cannot be done on the TI-81.) To do this, select **2:Delete** from the **MEMORY** menu. You are presented with a list of types of data. For example, if you wish to reset certain matrices, highlight **Matrix...** and press [ENTER]. Use the up and down arrow keys to move the selection cursor (▶) next to the item you want to delete, and then press [ENTER].

Continued on next page

CALCULATOR INSTRUCTIONS

Clearing Previous Entries

Only the TI-83 allows you to clear the previous entries from memory. To do this, select **3:Clear Entries** from the **MEMORY** menu. However, you cannot clear the last-answer variable **Ans**.

Linking Calculators

(This feature is not available on the TI-81.)

The TI-82 and TI-83 have a port that allows them to connect and communicate with another TI-82 or TI-83 or with a computer. The TI-83 also has special features to enable certain communication with a TI-82. This connection can be used to transfer variables, data lists, or programs to another calculator. The software that enables this communication is built into the calculator.

To connect two calculators, firmly insert either end of the black connecting cable into the port at the bottom of your calculator. Insert the other end into the other calculator's port. (Be sure to press each plug in firmly, because most errors are due to this incomplete connection.)

Transmitting Items

Begin by selecting items to transmit from the sending unit. Press [2nd] [LINK] to display the **SEND RECEIVE** menu. (A screen shot from a TI-83 is shown here. The TI-82 looks similar, but with fewer options.)

Select the menu item that identifies the data type to send. Each option will display a **SELECT** screen with no data selected, except for the option **1:All+** (**1:SelectAll+...** on the TI-82).

Use the arrow keys to move the selection cursor to an item you want to select (or deselect) and press [ENTER]. Selected names are marked with a ■. Use the arrow keys to continue moving up or down to select or deselect additional items.

Continued on next page

CALCULATOR INSTRUCTIONS

```
SEND RECEIVE
1:Receive
```

Press [2nd] [LINK] followed by the right-arrow key on the receiving calculator to display the **SEND RECEIVE** heading. Press the right arrow key to highlight **RECEIVE**. Select **1:Receive** to prepare the calculator to receive transmitted items. The message **Waiting...** will be displayed.

To transmit the selected data, go back to the sending unit and press the right-arrow key to highlight **TRANSMIT**. Press [ENTER] to select **1:Transmit**. The names and types of each selected item will be displayed line by line, first on the sending unit and then on the receiving unit as each item is accepted.

Linking the Calculator to a Macintosh or PC

With the TI-GRAPH LINK™ software and connecting cable, you can send and retrieve information between your TI-82 or TI-83 and your computer. (This feature is not available for the TI-81.)

After connecting your calculator to your computer, you can transfer graphs, screen images, programs, and data sets either from the calculator to the computer or from the computer to the calculator. It is easier to edit on the computer (long programming instructions, for example) and then transfer the information to the calculator. If information is in the computer, it can be printed or merged into other electronic documents. Programs and data files can be backed up to prevent accidental loss, and they can be shared with other calculators.

Setting Up

The TI-82 and TI-83 must use their own version of the TI-GRAPH LINK software. When installing the TI-GRAPH LINK software on your computer, be sure to install the TI-GRAPH LINK custom fonts.

To connect the cable between your computer and your calculator, connect one end of the TI-GRAPH LINK cable to a serial port on your computer and the other end to the port at the bottom of your calculator. Be sure to push in all connectors firmly.

After starting the appropriate TI-GRAPH LINK application, test your connection. From the **Link** menu, select **Get Screen**. (In the TI-82 software, select **Get LCD** in the **Receive** menu.) The contents of your calculator's display should appear in the window. This indicates that the communication link is okay. If you receive an error message, there is a communication problem. In this case, refer to the software's guidebook for instructions on how to solve the problem.

Continued on next page

CALCULATOR INSTRUCTIONS

Linking to the World Wide Web

You can use the TI-GRAPH LINK to import and export program and data files for file sharing on the Internet. If you have a connection to the World Wide Web, go to the Texas Instruments calculator home page at

www.ti.com/calc/docs/calchome.html

Here you will find customer support and services, as well as other useful information about the TI graphing calculator. Many calculator programs are available for download from the Texas Instruments Web site. The TI-GRAPH LINK software is also available here for free. However, you will still have to obtain the cables and connectors with which to link the calculator to the computer.

Calculator Guide for "Fireworks"

This brief unit provides many opportunities for students to explore functional relationships using the graphing calculator and to recall and practice many of the skills needed to work with this tool. Students will graph and create tables to investigate quadratic functions. Students can learn other calculator features, like finding an *x*-intercept or a root, as they work through the curriculum.

Although much of the mathematics in this unit is traditional in nature, the opportunities for students to develop their understanding are enhanced by the use of the graphing calculator. Strong connections are made between symbolic and graphical representations of quadratic situations. Furthermore, students contemplate and assess the importance and distinction of approximate versus exact results.

In the activity *The Ups and Downs of Quadratics* from Day 2, students explore the graphs of quadratic functions. More specifically, they investigate how changes in the coefficients of a quadratic function affect its graph. Additionally, this activity is an opportunity for students to refamiliarize themselves with the graphing capabilities of their calculator. *Function Graphing*, in the *TI Calculator Basics* section of this guide, contains general instructions about using the five graphing keys. Students who are unfamiliar with graphing calculators may find those instructions useful.

Day 3

The Day 3 discussion centers around graphs of quadratic equations. You may wish to use the graph of a quadratic on the calculator to discuss the nature of intercepts. Students may also point these out while studying a table generated by the calculator. (You cannot create tables on the TI-81.)

Later in the discussion, students create an equation to solve for an x-intercept. You may wish to remind students of the capability of their TI-82 or TI-83 to solve equations when one side is zero, as in the case of finding an x-intercept (or root). They can do the equivalent by graphing the expression and using the **TRACE** and **ZOOM** features to find a value so that the y-coordinate is equal to (or close to) zero. Also, students can use the TI-82 and TI-83 to calculate the x-intercept more accurately from the graph without needing to use **ZOOM**. The instructions in *Determining x-Intercepts, the Calculator Way* describe methods for finding an x-intercept using the graphing calculator.

Day 4

On Day 4, students again use the calculator to determine x-intercepts in order to develop a symbolic method that doesn't rely on graphing. Although the students might use the methods described in *Determining x-Intercepts, the Calculator Way,* the focus here is on building algebraic understanding based on factoring.

CALCULATOR INSTRUCTIONS

Determining x-Intercepts, the Calculator Way

You can use the TI-82 or TI-83 calculator to solve equations when one side of the equation is zero. The examples here show several methods for finding (at least approximately) an x-intercept of the function $h(t) = 160 + 92t - 16t^2$ from the activity *Factored Intercepts*.

To use the SOLVER feature on the TI-83, press MATH and then scroll down and select **0:Solver…**. The first screen should say **EQUATION SOLVER** across the top. If not, press the up arrow key once. Below the words **EQUATION SOLVER**, you'll find **eqn: 0=**. Enter your function here. After keying in **160+92X-16X²**, press ENTER.

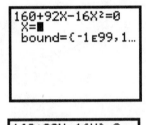

Your cursor should be at the **X=** as shown on the screen. Enter an estimate of where an x-intercept might be and then press ALPHA [SOLVE].

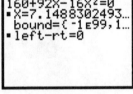

The next screen illustrates an example of what might result. Investigate what happens when you adjust the estimate you entered.

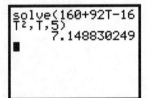

The TI-82 has a similar equation-solving feature, but the key sequence works differently. Press MATH and then scroll down and select **0:solve(**. This will cause **solve(** to appear on your home screen. To complete the command, enter the function, the variable, and a guess, separated by commas. Note the assumption that the function is equal to zero.

Another way to solve an equation is by graphing the related function and tracing to find a value so that y is equal to (or close to) zero.

Continued on next page

CALCULATOR INSTRUCTIONS

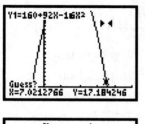

A third option is to instruct the calculator to determine the
x-intercept while working from a graph of the function. On the
TI-83 press [2nd] [CALC] and select **2:zero**. (On the TI-82 press
[2nd] [CALC] and select **2:root**.) Next, the calculator will request
guidance for its calculation algorithm by asking first for a left and
right bound and then for a guess between the two. Move the
cursor along the graph using the arrow keys, and press [ENTER] in
response to each prompt. After these three prompts are entered,
the calculator will display the *x*-value of the intercept.

Days 5–11

Although most activities on these days do not require the use of a graphing calculator, a graph or table can be used to help determine if two functions are equivalent. You may wish to challenge students by asking them how they can show that two expressions, one in standard form and one factored, are equivalent.

Challenging students to test for equivalence may be helpful when they must change the *Fireworks* function from standard to vertex form.

Day 7

The class activity on this day, *The Same but Different,* requires students to use the graphing calculators. *Function Graphing,* in the *TI Calculator Basics* section of this guide, reviews the techniques for graphing, tracing, and zooming. Encourage students to make thoughtful decisions about the accuracy of their tracing results when determining the vertex.

Day 8

As suggested in the *Teacher's Guide* for *Fireworks,* encourage students to graph differing responses to *Homework 7: Make Your Own Vertices.* Discuss the results. This is a good opportunity to strengthen the connections between algebraic and geometric thinking.

Students may attempt to graph or create a table for the vertex form of a quadratic by entering $Y_1=A(X-H)^2+K$. This will most likely generate a graph and table based upon whatever values have previously been stored in memory for the variables A, H, and K. Thus, the results likely will be different for each student. You can use this general equation for Y_1 to get more meaningful results by having students store specific values in each of those cells.

Students should have access to graphing calculators during the in-class assessment. This might raise concerns about students using information that appears on the screen or is in the calculator's memory.

Be assured that for the in-class assessment for *Fireworks,* there is no particular reason to clear calculator screens or reset memory between classes or if students share calculators. It is unlikely that any information that remained on the calculators would be of significant assistance to students. In any case, the emphasis in IMP assessments is on having students communicate what they know about mathematical concepts, so they should be expected to explain their work and justify their conclusions.

Appendix A

Supplemental Problems

The supplemental problems provide many opportunities for students to use the calculator's graphing capabilities. Students ready for the algebraic challenges can still test expressions for equivalence using the calculator's graph or table.

Students working on *Imagine a Solution* or *Number Research* might be curious about the calculator's complex number features. (Press MATH and select the CPX menu.) The TI-83 also offers a complex number mode, which you could let students investigate on their own.

Calculator Guide for "Orchard Hideout"

This unit focuses mainly on geometric and algebraic concepts and does not require any significant new uses of the graphing calculator. However, the unit provides several new applications for familiar calculator features, as well as opportunities to explore new features. Students may wish to use the calculator's programming and graphing abilities while solving problems. The picturesque nature of the unit's geometry may spark some students to investigate the drawing features of the calculator as well.

Students will use the calculator daily for many varied computational purposes, in addition to use of the sine, cosine, and tangent functions. For a review of the calculator's basic computational features, see the *TI Calculator Basics* section.

Day 1

The Day 1 activity encourages students to develop models to create a picture of what the orchard might look like. Students may wish to use the drawing features of the graphing calculator to create a smaller version of the orchard. *Drawing an Orchard* gives instructions for creating a simple model on the graphing calculator. You may find such drawing useful for class discussion on Day 1 or later in the unit. But hold off giving these instructions to students until later in the unit, or give them only to students who request them.

Similar work with the drawing features will allow students to investigate trees of different sizes. This will be helpful during the Day 4 activity *More Mini-Orchards. Programming an Orchard Hideout* in this guide gives specific instructions for a program to draw various orchard models.

Once you draw a picture on the graphing calculator, you can save it with the command **StorePic**. (The TI-81 cannot store pictures.) Press [2nd] [DRAW], move the cursor right to **STO**. Then press [ENTER] since **1:StorePic** is already highlighted.

Next, press [VARS], select **4:Picture...**, and select the memory location to store this picture. (You might choose the memory location according to the radius of the orchard.) The location you choose, such as **Pic1**, will appear on the home screen after the **StorePic** command, as shown here. Be sure to press [ENTER] one more time to carry out your **StorePic Pic1** command.

You can retrieve a stored picture using the command **RecallPic**. Press [2nd] [DRAW], move the cursor right to **STO**, and select **2:RecallPic**. Find **Pic1** (or whatever picture name you want to recall) in the **VARS** menu in the same way as just described.

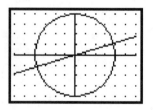

Students can also incorporate a line of sight into their drawing with a simple linear equation entered in the [Y=] editor (rather than using the **DRAW** menu as suggested in *Drawing an Orchard*). Once the linear equation has been entered, give the **Circle(** command. The screen shown here is a radius-4 orchard with the linear equation **Y₁=0.3X**.

CALCULATOR INSTRUCTIONS

Drawing an Orchard

You can construct a simple drawing to represent an orchard using the DRAW and GRAPH features of the graphing calculator. You can also make adjustments to this "starter orchard" to represent orchards of different sizes. (This cannot be done on the TI-81 because it has no circle-drawing option.)

Keep in mind that there is a limit to the exactness of this model. It is restricted by the location of the pixels on the TI calculator's screen. The pixels will cause discrepancies in the spacing of parts of the drawing, especially trees.

These instructions create an orchard of radius 6. First make all functions in the Y= editor inactive by deselecting the = sign for each function.

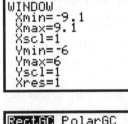

Next make the viewing window "square" by pressing WINDOW and adjusting the window variables to match the screen shown here. For this drawing, it means a circle will look like a circle. (Disregard **Xres** on the TI-82.)

Next, set the graph format to draw a grid. These grid dots will represent the trees in our drawing. On the TI-83, press 2nd [FORMAT] to get the graph format screen. Highlight settings as shown. On the TI-82, press WINDOW and then move the cursor to the right to highlight the **FORMAT** menu.

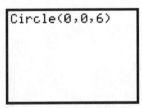

The final step is to draw the circular outline of the orchard. Go to the home screen to enter this command (press 2nd [QUIT]). The **Circle(** command is in the **DRAW** menu. Press 2nd [DRAW], scroll down to **9:Circle(**, and press ENTER. Type **0,0,6** for the center and radius of the circle.

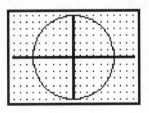

When you press ENTER, your result should look like what's shown here. You might also draw a line segment (line of sight) through this picture by defining the coordinates of the start and end. The line command is in the **DRAW** menu.

In the activity *More Mini-Orchards,* students investigate what tree radius will create a hideout in smaller, simpler orchards than the one in the central unit problem. If students are interested in the drawing features or in programming their calculator, encourage them to draw a model of a small orchard on their graphing calculator. Or you may prefer to use a visual with the class to explore different conditions for the orchard.

Programming an Orchard Hideout gives specific instructions for a program to simulate various orchard and tree sizes. It is included here primarily for your convenience rather than as instructions for students. You may find it a useful addition to class discussions to display the program on the overhead. The program is not too long and will run on the TI-82 and TI-83. However, be aware that even orchards of a modest size will take quite some time to draw.

Review *Programming the Calculator,* in the *TI Calculator Basics* section in this guide, for general instructions on how to program a TI graphing calculator.

If you have students who are interested or skilled in programming, ask them to design an orchard on the calculator themselves. This would be a challenging project for an interested student, and the results might prove creative.

CALCULATOR INSTRUCTIONS

Programming an Orchard Hideout

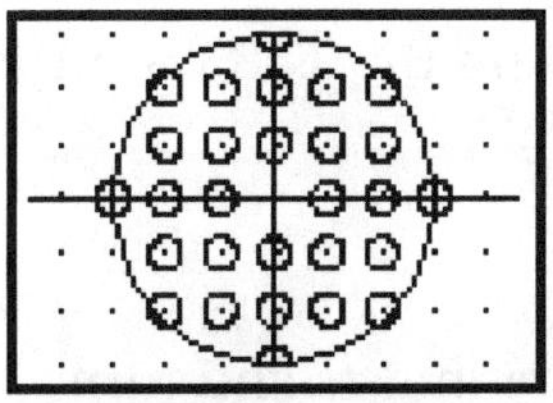

The following program models orchards with different radii and different tree sizes. The screen shot to the left shows a radius-3 orchard with trees of radius 0.30 units.

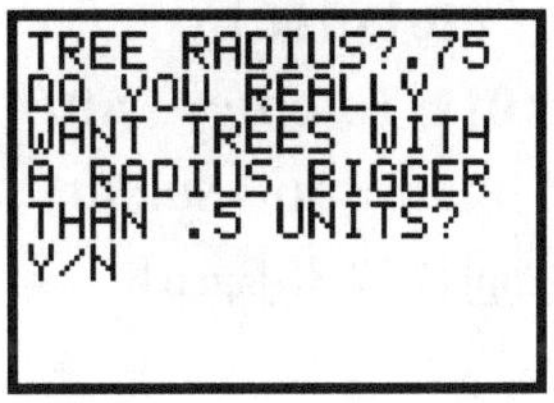

The program allows you to select the radius of the orchard and the radius of the trees in the orchard. You will be asked to confirm if you select a tree radius larger than half a unit. You also can select to have the lattice grid on or off in the final drawing.

Recall that the calculator is limited in its drawings (and graphs) by the location of the liquid crystal display (LCD) pixels. These drawings may not be useful for exact measurements, but they can serve to help explore these varying orchard conditions.

To enter the program instructions, you must first be in the PRGM editor (refer to *Programming the Calculator* in this guide). Enter the steps for the program from the column on the left. The column on the right explains each programming instruction. The text immediately beneath each bar helps to summarize different parts of the program.

Instruction	Explanation
	These first commands prepare the calculator's graphing window.
:1→Xscl	
:1→Yscl	Press STO▸ for the →. Find Xscl by pressing VARS and selecting 1:Window... and then 3:Xscl. Find Yscl in the same way as Xscl. These two commands set the *x*- and *y*-scales to 1 for use with the calculator's grid command. (The user will later have the option to place a dot at every lattice point.)

Continued on next page

CALCULATOR INSTRUCTIONS

:GridOff

:AxesOn

These two commands set up the graphing screen for drawing the orchard. Find them in the [2nd] [FORMAT] menu on the TI-83 or in the [WINDOW] **FORMAT** menu on the TI-82.

:PlotsOff

:FnOff

These two commands eliminate plotting of data in lists and turn off any expressions in the function editor. Enter **PlotsOff** by pressing [2nd] [STAT PLOT] and selecting **4: PlotsOff**. To enter **FnOff** on the TI-83, press [VARS], highlight the **Y-VARS** menu, and select **On/Off** and then **2:FnOff**. For the TI-82, press [2nd] [Y-VARS] and select **On/Off**, and then select **FnOff**.

:ClrDraw

Clears any previous drawing. Find **ClrDraw** in the [2nd] [DRAW] menu.

The next section contains commands that allow the user to input the radius of the orchard.

:ClrHome

Clears the home screen. Find **ClrHome** in the [PRGM] **I/O** menu.

:Disp "ORCHARD RADIUS?"

:Disp "(WORKS BEST WITH"

:Disp "VALUES UNDER 8)"

:Input R

This group of instructions asks you to select the orchard radius and store the size in **R**. Find **Disp** and **Input** in the [PRGM] **I/O** menu. Press [ALPHA] [␣] to enter a space between the words, and press [ALPHA] ["] for a quotation mark.

:abs(R)→R

This command ensures that the rest of the program uses a positive value for **R**. Find **abs(** in the [MATH] **NUM** menu on the TI-83. Press [2nd] [ABS] on the TI-82.

:Lbl A

This label is a marker to return to if the user chooses to change the tree radius. Find **Lbl** in the [PRGM] **CTL** menu.

Continued on next page

CALCULATOR INSTRUCTIONS

These commands allow the user to select a tree radius. If the radius selected is larger than 0.5, the calculator will ask if the user wishes to change the radius.

:ClrHome

:Input "TREE RADIUS?",T   Asks the user to input the tree radius, and stores that value in **T**.

:abs(T)→T

:If T>.5   Find **If** in the [PRGM] **CTL** menu. Find **>** in the [2nd] [TEST] menu.

:Then   Find **Then** in the [PRGM] **CTL** menu.

:Disp "DO YOU REALLY"

:Disp "WANT TREES WITH"

:Disp "A RADIUS BIGGER"

:Disp "THAN .5 UNITS?"

:Input "YES(1)/NO(0)?",E   This set of instructions gives the program user a chance to reevaluate a tree radius choice that may cause trees to drastically overlap. Use [÷] for "**/**".

:If E≠1   Find **≠** in the [2nd] [TEST] menu.

:Goto A   If the user enters anything but **Y**, returns to label A to ask for the tree radius again. Find **Goto** in the [PRGM] **CTL** menu.

:END   Ends the if-then statement. Press [PRGM] and scroll down for **END**.

This section asks whether the user would like to display a lattice grid.

:Menu("LATTICE G

RID?","ON",B,"OF

F",C)   This is a single, long line of code that the calculator will wrap around the screen. **Menu** is a command that allows users to select their choice from a screen menu. Depending on the user's selection, the program will go to Label B or Label C. Find **Menu** in the [PRGM] **CTL** menu.

Continued on next page

`:Lbl B`

`:GridOn`

Find **GridOn** in the [2nd] [FORMAT] screen on the TI-83, or in the [WINDOW] **FORMAT** menu on the TI-82.

This section contains instructions for the calculator to actually draw the orchard.

`:Lbl C`

`:R→Ymax`

`:-R→Ymin`

`:1.516*R→Xmax`

`:-1.516*R→Xmin`

These four commands set an approximate square window based on the radius of the orchard. "Square" means a circle will appear as a circle. Find **Ymax** by pressing [VARS], select **1:Window**, and then select from the **X/Y** menu, and find the others similarly.

`:Circle(0,0,R)`

Draws a circle of radius **R** centered at (0,0). Find **Circle(** by pressing [2nd] [DRAW] and scrolling down the **DRAW** menu.

This set of commands draws a tree at each of the lattice points inside the given orchard, excluding the point (0,0).

`:For(X,-R,R)`

`:For(Y,-R,R)`

The first of these **For** loops steps **X** from –R to R, that is, from left to right across the orchard. For each **X** value, the second **For** loop then steps **Y** from –R to R. Together, the two loops step through every lattice point in the orchard's circumscribed square. Find **For(** in the [PRGM] **CTL** menu.

`:If X²+Y²≤R² and`

`(X≠0 or Y≠0)`

This test runs every time through the loop to see if the (**X**, **Y**) coordinates fall inside the orchard but are not (0,0). Nothing will happen if either "$X^2+Y^2 \leq R^2$" or "$X \neq 0$ or $Y \neq 0$" is false. Find **or** and **and** by pressing [2nd] [TEST] and highlighting **LOGIC**.

Continued on next page

CALCULATOR INSTRUCTIONS

:Circle(X,Y,T)

If both **If** conditions are true, this instruction draws a circle (tree) of radius **T** with center (**X, Y**).

:End

Identifies the end of the inner (the **Y** value) **For** loop. For the **End** command, press PRGM. **CTL** will already be highlighted. Select **7↓End**.

:End

Identifies the end of the outer (the **X** value) **For** loop.

In the discussion of *Homework 4: In, On, or Out?*, students develop an equation or equations to describe a circle, for example, $x^2 + y^2 = 10^2$. Students may wish to graph this on the graphing calculator. Doing so will offer an opportunity to revisit the definition of a function and to create the need for symbolic manipulation in order to enter this equation in the $\boxed{Y=}$ function editor.

Students will quickly discover that graphing $\texttt{Y1=}\sqrt{(10^2-X^2)}$ causes two problems. The first problem is that you see only half (the top half) of the circle. The equation $x^2 + y^2 = 10^2$ does not represent a function, but the equation $y = \sqrt{10^2 - x^2}$ does. Students will recognize that graphing $\texttt{Y2=}^-\sqrt{(10^2-X^2)}$ will complete the circle. (Note that a similar topic, the standard equation of a circle, comes up on Day 19.)

The second problem is that the "circle" may not look like a circle. The calculator displays a viewing window as set by the user in the $\boxed{\text{WINDOW}}$ menu. Unless these window values are specifically chosen to create x distances to be visually equal to y distances, the graph appears stretched. You can quickly fix this by pressing $\boxed{\text{ZOOM}}$ and selecting $\texttt{5:ZSquare}$.

When students discuss whether the distance formula they created in *Homework 6: The Distance Formula* holds true for points with negative coordinates, expect some to ask, "Why does my calculator show -3^2 as equal to -9?" The order of operations that the TI calculator follows will first square the value 3 and then apply the negative sign to the resulting square.

Encourage students to review what squaring means, and remind them that entering $(-3)^2$ gives the square of -3.

Day 12

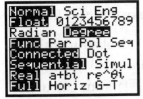

Students may use trigonometric ratios to help solve for the area and circumference of a hexagon. But they may question the reasonableness of some of their results. Remember, a potential trouble spot is that the mode may be set to radians rather than degrees. To set the calculator to degrees, press [MODE] and highlight **Degree**, as shown here.

Day 16

The *Teacher's Guide* for *Orchard Hideout* suggests reminding students to take advantage of the last-answer memory feature to use the calculator's multidigit values from one calculation to the next. Although the focus of *Homework 15: Orchard Growth Revisited* is on geometry as opposed to the complexities of significant digits, students who are fairly new to the TI graphing calculator may find *Using* [ANS] *and the Last Entry* helpful.

Here's another quick note for today about the differences between calculators regarding order of operations. Students using the TI-83 may mistakenly calculate $\frac{2.5}{2\pi}$ as equal to (approximately) 3.93 because they neglected to enclose 2π in parentheses. The TI-81 and TI-82 do not require these parentheses to calculate and display correctly **2.5/2π** as equal to .398. On the TI-83, enter **2.5/(2π)** to correctly determine the approximate decimal value of this fraction.

CALCULATOR INSTRUCTIONS

Using [ANS] and the Last Entry

You can recall the answer to the last calculation and use it to continue calculations on your TI calculator. This may be more convenient than keying in a long decimal value from the previous answer and more accurate than keying in only some digits of that answer.

Your calculator stores the last answer in **Ans**. You can use the variable **Ans** to represent the last answer in most places. Place **Ans** in the cursor location by pressing [2nd] [ANS] (above the [(-)] key).

You can use **Ans** as the first entry of the next calculation without having to press [2nd] [ANS]. If you begin a new line with a function or operation key (such as [+], [−], [×], [÷], [x^2], or [$\wedge$]), your calculator will automatically insert **Ans**.

```
2.5/(2π)
           .3978873577
12²*π-Ans²*π
           451.8919829
Ans/1.5
           301.2613219
■
```

You can use this last-answer recall to help keep track of all the multidigit values while solving *Homework 15: Orchard Growth Revisited*. One potential series of entries may look like the screen shown here.

An alternative method for keeping the multidigit values is to store the result of a calculation into a variable before you evaluate another expression. To store a value, press [STO▸] (this creates the → on screen) followed by a variable name.

```
           .3978873577
Ans²*π
           .4973591972
Ans→A
           .4973591972
12²*π
           452.3893421
Ans-A■
```

For example, you may want to remember the cross-sectional area of the original tree to use in later calculations. After calculating the cross-sectional area of the original tree (≈ 0.497 square inches), store the value into variable **A**. In the next step, after calculating the cross-sectional area of the tree with a trunk radius of 1 foot (≈ 452.39 square inches), you can find the required increase in cross-sectional area by evaluating **Ans−A**. Your calculator will display the result of this expression as **451.8919829**.

If students discover the greatest common divisor (GCD) idea associated with *POW 4: A Marching Strip,* they may ask if their calculator has that feature. Only the TI-83 has the GCD built in. Press MATH, highlight **NUM**, and select **9:gcd(**. To complete the command, enter the two values for which you wish to find the GCD. For example, to find the GCD of 63 and 90, enter **gcd(63,90)** and press ENTER. The result, 9, will be displayed.

A frustrated TI-82 or TI-81 user may be motivated to write a GCD program!

Appendix A

Supplemental Problems

The majority of the supplemental problems explore geometric ideas, and they are not dependent on graphing calculators. If students use them to calculate trigonometric ratios, you might need to remind them to check that their calculators are in degree mode.

Appendix B

Blackline Masters

The sections *Drawing an Orchard* and *Programming an Orchard Hideout* in this guide may also be useful in the classroom if you have access to a TI graphing calculator connected to an overhead projector.

Calculator Guide for "Meadows or Malls?"

This unit is a true reflection of how the nature of important mathematics is affected by today's powerful technology. *Meadows or Malls?* presents students with a complex linear programming problem involving six variables and six equations. The TI graphing calculator's ability to quickly manipulate matrices is essential to the unit. Through the use of the calculator, solving systems of equations becomes a much simpler task.

Students will experience linear programming at a level of complexity for which pencil-and-paper methods may prove unwieldy for both graphing and solving equations. It is possible to use paper and pencil, but the calculator allows students to concentrate on more sophisticated questions rather than on the mechanics. Once students learn how to enter matrices into the calculator, they can do matrix operations, such as addition, multiplication, and inversion, on the calculator. The matrix inversion feature of the graphing calculator will help students solve the unit problem.

Like *Orchard Hideout,* much of this unit further develops coordinate geometry's connection to algebraic ideas, focusing especially on three-dimensional geometry. Few calculator skills are needed during these stages. However, students may recall that the calculator has graphing capabilities that can be used to solve two-variable systems of equations.

Several students likely will recall working with the calculator to graph the linear equations defined by the constraints of *Homework 2: Heavy Flying*. If not, there is no particular need to push students to remember the techniques. You may elect to provide students with the calculator instructions *Solving Systems by Graphing* following Day 4. You may also want to review *Function Graphing* from the *TI Graphing Calculator Basics* section in this guide.

As just mentioned, students may want to use the graphing calculator to help them solve two-variable linear programming problems. *Solving Systems by Graphing* will summarize the graphing calculator techniques for solving these types of problems. You may decide to use this in conjunction with *Ideas for Solving Systems* provided in the student text. Notice that the examples illustrate the equations from *Homework 2: Heavy Flying*.

CALCULATOR INSTRUCTIONS

Solving Systems by Graphing

You can use the graphing calculator to estimate the coordinates for the point at which the graphs of two equations intersect. This is the same as finding the common solution to a pair of equations.

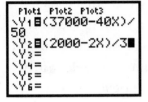

If you used other variables in your equations, you will need to replace them with X and Y and solve for Y in order to enter the equations into the $\boxed{Y=}$ screen of the calculator. For example, in working with the situation for *Homework 2: Heavy Flying,* you might use X to represent the number of containers of chicken feed and Y to represent the number of cartons of calculators. If so, the equations corresponding to the weight and volume constraints can be entered as shown here.

You will also need to set the calculator's viewing screen appropriately using $\boxed{WINDOW}$ (or $\boxed{RANGE}$ on the TI-81), considering the values of the variables that are meaningful in the situation.

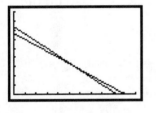

Graph the equations you have entered by pressing $\boxed{GRAPH}$. Using a combination of $\boxed{TRACE}$ and $\boxed{ZOOM}$, you can determine with reasonable accuracy the X- and Y-coordinates at which these equations intersect.

A nice tracing feature on the TI is the **ZoomInteger** command found in the $\boxed{ZOOM}$ menu. After selecting this command, you'll be returned to the graph screen. Move the cursor to a central location and press $\boxed{ENTER}$. Now your calculator will trace only for integer values of X. The TI-82 and TI-83 have a **ZoomDecimal** command that allows you to trace by tenths. Using these tracing features may make it simpler to determine a point of intersection.

Continued on next page

CALCULATOR INSTRUCTIONS

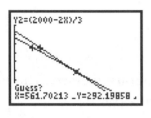

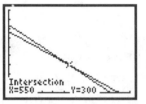

However, the TI-82 and TI-83 offer one more option that greatly simplifies this whole process. Press [2nd] [CALC], highlight **5:intersect**, and press [ENTER].

Now that you are returned to the graph, you must answer each prompt that appears. You first need to identify the equations whose intersection you will find, which is easy if there are only two graphs on the screen. The equation for the first equation you graphed will appear at the top of the screen, and you select it by pressing [ENTER]. The other equation will then appear, and you again press [ENTER]. (If there are more than two graphs on the screen, you can move among them using the up and down arrow keys.)

To reply to the **Guess?** prompt, simply place the cursor near the point of intersection. (The left and right arrow keys will move it along the graph of the equation that is currently displayed.) Then press [ENTER] one more time to have the calculator determine the point of intersection.

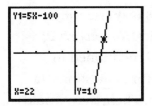

While discussing *Homework 8: How Much After How Long?*, use the graphing and tracing features of the TI calculator to explore the relationships between the situations and the ordered pairs of the associated functions. The screen here shows an ordered pair found while tracing the function **Y₁=5X-100**. Refer to *Function Graphing* in the *TI Calculator Basics* section in this guide to review these features. Be sure to replace the independent variable with **X** and the dependent variable with **Y** on the calculator. After setting up the graph, press [ZOOM] and select **8:ZInteger**. Doing this will allow you to trace only integer values for **X**, which may be helpful in this activity.

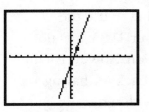

During the discussion of *Homework 14: Fitting a Line,* you may find that some students have used the regression capabilities of the graphing calculator even though that is not the expectation here. (Regression is not an official part of the curriculum until Year 4.) Even if students come up with such a calculator technique for solving the problem, they should still be expected to understand the noncalculator technique being developed in the activity.

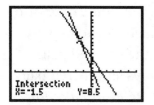

Again, as mentioned in Day 15, some students may use the calculator to help solve problems like those in *Homework 25: Fitting More Lines*. In addition to the method mentioned in Day 15, students might graph the equations from Questions 1a and 2a to determine the point of intersection. Then, they would use these coordinates for *a* and *b* when completing Question 3a. (The same method could be used for Question 4 as well.) The emphasis in this homework (and similar assignments) is on the idea that solving the pair of equations from Questions 1 and 2 leads to a linear function that goes through both (3, 4) and (5, 1).

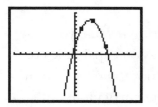

Not to sound like a broken record, but some students may solve *Homework 27: Fitting Quadratics* by choosing to use the quadratic regression capabilities of the TI-82 or TI-83. It is not necessary to bring these ideas to their attention. However, if any students bring it out, give them a pat on the back for having connected ideas from statistics and algebra within the mathematics of this problem.

Day 30

Entering Matrices and Doing Matrix Arithmetic demonstrates the mechanics of working with matrices on the TI calculator. It includes instructions on how to enter a matrix into the calculator and do simple matrix arithmetic. These instructions will assist students with *Calculators to the Rescue.*

Students will work with matrices throughout the remainder of the unit. You might encourage them to save these instructions for later reference.

CALCULATOR INSTRUCTIONS

Entering Matrices and Doing Matrix Arithmetic

The TI graphing calculator will allow you to enter matrices and perform many operations with matrices. You can display or edit a matrix in the matrix editor. You can use many of the calculator's mathematics functions, as long as the dimensions of the matrix are appropriate.

The TI-83 has ten matrix variables, **[A]** through **[J]**, and each can have up to 99 rows or columns depending on how much memory is available. The TI-82 is similar but has only five matrix variables, **[A]** through **[E]**. The TI-81 has three matrix variables, each of which can accommodate a maximum of six rows and columns.

These instructions will guide you through *Calculators to the Rescue,* which uses matrices created in *Homework 29: Fresh Ingredients.*

```
NAMES MATH EDIT
1:[A]
2:[B]
3:[C]
4:[D]
5:[E]
6:[F]
7↓[G]
```

To enter a matrix into your calculator, you must get to your calculator's matrix editor. Press [MATRX] and highlight **EDIT**. Press [ENTER] if you would like to store the matrix in **[A]**.

```
MATRIX[A] 2 ×3
[0        0      0     ]
[0        0      0     ]


1,1=0
```

Before making your matrix entries, you must define the matrix dimensions. The Woos' baking plan matrix in Question 1 of *Calculators to the Rescue* is a 2 × 3 matrix, so press [2] [ENTER] [3] [ENTER]. You can edit any mistakes by using the arrow keys to highlight what you want to change and entering over it.

Unlike the TI-81, the TI-82 and TI-83 display the matrix in its exact form, as shown in the preceding screen illustration. Unless used previously, all entries in the matrix will appear as **0**. As you move through the matrix, notice how the calculator identifies the row and column at the bottom of the screen.

(The TI-81 will create a list identifying the row and column for all entries. In addition, a pixel image of the matrix flashes the location of the entry you are currently editing. Watch how it changes as you move through the row and column title for each entry.)

Continued on next page

CALCULATOR INSTRUCTIONS

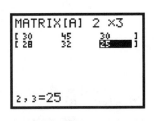

Enter the Woos' baking plan matrix by keying in each entry and then pressing ENTER. You will move to the right through the first row. After the third entry, you'll go to the second row, and so on.

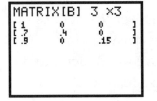

Press MATRX, and highlight **EDIT** in order to enter the next matrix. Follow the same steps to enter the Woos' amount matrix and cost matrix. Be sure to enter the amount matrix as matrix **[B]** and the cost matrix as matrix **[C]**.

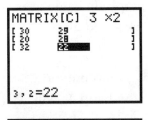

Instruct the calculator to do arithmetic with matrices as you would give any other arithmetic command. Go to the home screen by typing 2nd [QUIT]. Enter the matrix variables by pressing MATRX and selecting from the **NAMES** menu. Press ENTER after highlighting the matrix name you wish to place in the home screen.

(On the TI-81, the matrix variables are the secondary function on the 1, 2, and 3 keys.)

Note: The brackets found as the secondary function above the × and – keys *cannot* be used in conjunction with letters to enter matrix names. The calculator will report a syntax error if a matrix variable name is entered in this manner.

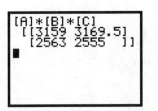

To calculate the total cost matrix for the Woos, you must calculate **[A]** * **[B]** * **[C]**. (The calculator will multiply correctly even if you do not enter the multiplication symbol between the matrix variable names.) This screen shows the final step of *Calculators to the Rescue*.

Investigate how the calculator responds when you try to multiply matrices in which the column and row dimensions do not match.

Day 33

As you wrap up the discussion of *Finding an Inverse* and introduce the notation $[A]^{-1}$, some curious students are likely to investigate the command $[A]^{-1}$. They will discover that it does work. Although the *Teacher's Guide* suggests delaying this discussion until the following day, it may prove too difficult to do that if students exhibit a strong interest in this feature.

Clearly, this is a powerful capability of the TI graphing calculator. Students quickly appreciate the amount of work saved after having just completed *Finding an Inverse*.

For *Homework 33: Inverses and Equations,* we recommend that you have students try to compute the inverses by hand. It will contribute to their understanding of how Question 2 relates to Question 1. (It is also the case that every student may not have access at home to graphing calculators.)

Day 34

Before students begin the activity *Calculators Again,* you might use an overhead projector calculator to demonstrate how to determine the inverse of a matrix. The instructions in *Finding the Inverse of a Matrix* in this guide may be helpful for students to use during your demonstration or as a reference while they work.

Calculators Again is worked through for your reference on Day 35 in this guide.

The calculator instructions in the section *Solving Linear Systems Using Matrices* in this guide summarize the entire process for translating a system of linear equations into a matrix equation and solving the matrix equation using a matrix inverse. These instructions are based on the system from *Homework 19: Gardener's Dilemma*. Because it may be more valuable for students to summarize their steps by writing these instructions themselves, you might hold off on making these instructions available to students.

Refer to the section *Matrices: Shortcuts and Tips* for more ideas about working with matrices on the TI graphing calculator.

Finding the Inverse of a Matrix

You have found that by solving a system of equations, you can determine the inverse of a matrix. You can also use the TI graphing calculator to find the inverse of a matrix.

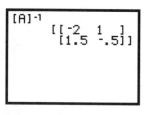

1. Enter the matrix you wish to invert into one of the calculator's matrix variables. The example here shows the matrix variable **[A]** being defined as $\begin{bmatrix} 1 & 2 \\ 3 & 4 \end{bmatrix}$.

2. Press [2nd] [QUIT] to return to the home screen.

3. Press [MATRX]. The matrix **[A]**, which you wish to use, will already be highlighted, so just press [ENTER]. (On the TI-81, press [2nd] [[A]] for matrix **[A]**.)

4. To get the $^{-1}$, press [x^{-1}].

5. Complete the command by pressing [ENTER].

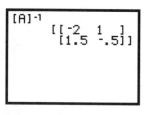

Notice how the results are displayed like a 2 × 2 matrix on the calculator's screen. A **[** indicates the beginning of a row, and a **]** indicates the end. The TI-82 and TI-83 also insert an extra set of brackets to show the beginning and end of the matrix.

Attempt to ask the calculator for the inverse of a noninvertible matrix, such as $\begin{bmatrix} 1 & 2 \\ 2 & 4 \end{bmatrix}$. Note the error message, and then select **Goto** to observe what the calculator identifies as the cause.

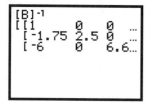

Next, invert a 3 × 3 matrix. The screen here shows the inverse of the matrix **[B]** defined as

$$\begin{bmatrix} 1 & 0 & 0 \\ .7 & .4 & 0 \\ .9 & 0 & .15 \end{bmatrix}$$

The ellipses to the right indicate additional information. Use the arrow keys to scroll the matrix.

CALCULATOR INSTRUCTIONS

Solving Linear Systems Using Matrices

These instructions will guide you through the steps needed to solve a system of linear equations using the calculator's matrix capabilities.

Recall that a system of linear equations can be written as a matrix equation in the form [A] [X] = [B], where [A] is the *coefficient matrix,* [X] is a column matrix made up of the variables in the system, and [B] is a column matrix called the *constant term matrix.* Solving the matrix equation for [X] will solve for the variables of the system of linear equations.

This matrix equation can be solved by multiplying both sides by the inverse of matrix [A]. The resulting equations, $[X] = [A]^{-1}[B]$, states that the variables that make up column matrix [X] are equal to the entries of the column matrix that is a result of the multiplication $[A]^{-1}[B]$.

To solve the system of linear equations, you can use your calculator to find $[A]^{-1}[B]$.

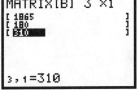

Begin by entering the coefficient matrix and column matrix into two separate matrix variables. The calculator's matrix variables **[A]** and **[B]** are convenient to use for this example. The values in the screen illustrations are taken from the matrix equation in *Homework 19: Gardener's Dilemma.*

$$900L + 120F + 40S = 1865$$
$$160F + 800S = 180$$
$$120L + 80F + 240S = 310$$

Be sure to place a 0 in the second row of [A] because L is not part of the second equation.

Thus, the matrix equation you wish to solve is:

$$\begin{bmatrix} 900 & 120 & 40 \\ 0 & 160 & 800 \\ 120 & 80 & 240 \end{bmatrix} \begin{bmatrix} L \\ F \\ S \end{bmatrix} = \begin{bmatrix} 1865 \\ 180 \\ 310 \end{bmatrix}$$

Continued on next page

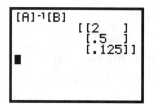

CALCULATOR INSTRUCTIONS

[A]⁻¹[B]
        [[2   ]
        [.5   ]
        [.125]]

After defining the matrices **[A]** and **[B]**, press 2nd [QUIT] to return to the home screen. Press MATRX (**1: [A]** will be highlighted already) and press ENTER. Press x^{-1} MATRX, highlight **2: [B]**, and press ENTER. Your home screen should look like the first line of the screen shown here. Now, simply press ENTER, and the calculator will display the result of multiplying the inverse of the coefficient matrix and the constant term matrix. Each entry of the column matrix displayed is equal to the corresponding variable of the original system of equations.

$$\begin{bmatrix} L \\ F \\ S \end{bmatrix} = \begin{bmatrix} 2 \\ .5 \\ .125 \end{bmatrix}$$

CALCULATOR INSTRUCTIONS

Matrices: Shortcuts and Tips

You can enter, edit, and store matrices in the matrix editor. You can also do these tasks in the home screen on the TI-82 and TI-83 (but not the TI-81).

```
[[1,2][3,4]]+[[3
,-2][1,4]]
          [[4 0]
           [4 8]]
```

If you wish to add

$$\begin{bmatrix} 1 & 2 \\ 3 & 4 \end{bmatrix} + \begin{bmatrix} 3 & -2 \\ 1 & 4 \end{bmatrix},$$

enter the code as shown in the screen. For brackets, press 2nd [[ ] and 2nd [ ]]. Notice that the first **[** indicates the start of a matrix and the second **[** indicates the start of a row. Each row must end with a **]**, and each matrix must end with a **]** as well. Separate row entries with a comma (,). *Reminder:* You cannot use these brackets to enter the name of a matrix variable, such as **[A]**.

```
[[1,2][3,4]]→[A]
          [[1 2]
           [3 4]]
■
```

The ability to enter matrices in the home screen can be helpful when storing a matrix to a matrix variable. Enter the matrix, being careful to place the brackets in the correct places. Press STO▸, and then select the matrix variable from the MATRX **NAMES** menu.

```
5→[A](2,1):[A]
          [[1 2]
           [5 4]]
```

If you wish to change an entry in a matrix that has already been entered, enter the new entry (**5** in our example), press STO▸ MATRX , highlight the matrix name (**[A]** in our example), and press ENTER . This returns you to the home screen. Now, designate the row and column affected by the change (**2, 1** in our example) by pressing (2 , 1) ALPHA [:]. Press MATRX (**1: [A]** is already highlighted) and press ENTER ENTER to display matrix **[A]**.

Sometimes a matrix is too large to be seen on only one screen. Use the calculator's arrow keys to scroll through the matrix.

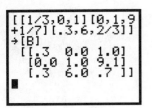

If the matrix rolls off the screen because of repeating decimals, you can always ask the calculator to round to one decimal place (or any other number of places). Press MODE and then highlight **1** instead of **Float**.

These comments and screen shots are intended as a reference for you in preparing for class discussion of *Calculators Again*.

Each system of linear equations can be set up in the equivalent matrix equation: $[A][X] = [B]$. Manipulating and then solving $[X] = [A]^{-1}[B]$ will calculate the values of the variables in the original system of linear equations. Use the calculator to evaluate $[A]^{-1}[B]$.

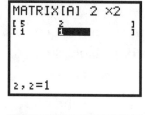

For the sake of convenience, each example here will store the coefficient matrix in $[A]$ and the constant term matrix in $[B]$.

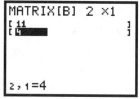

First, set up Question 1 as the equivalent matrix equation:

$\begin{bmatrix} 5 & 2 \\ 1 & 1 \end{bmatrix} \begin{bmatrix} d \\ e \end{bmatrix} = \begin{bmatrix} 11 \\ 4 \end{bmatrix}$. Enter $\begin{bmatrix} 5 & 2 \\ 1 & 1 \end{bmatrix}$ as **[A]** and $\begin{bmatrix} 11 \\ 4 \end{bmatrix}$ as **[B]**.

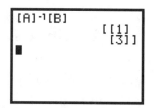

Evaluating **[A]⁻¹[B]** will solve for $\begin{bmatrix} d \\ e \end{bmatrix}$. As seen in this screen, $d = 1$ and $e = 3$.

For Question 2, solve $\begin{bmatrix} 2 & 3 & -1 \\ 1 & -2 & 4 \\ 4 & -1 & 7 \end{bmatrix} \begin{bmatrix} r \\ s \\ t \end{bmatrix} = \begin{bmatrix} 3 \\ 2 \\ 8 \end{bmatrix}$.

The first two screens below show the process of entering matrices [A] and [B]. The third screen shows the result of attempting to evaluate $[A]^{-1}[B]$. The calculator gives this message because [A] has no inverse.

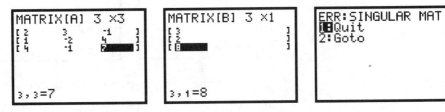

For Question 3, solve the matrix.

$$\begin{bmatrix} 4 & 1 & 2 & -3 \\ -3 & 1 & -1 & 4 \\ -1 & 2 & 5 & 1 \\ 5 & 4 & 3 & -1 \end{bmatrix} \begin{bmatrix} w \\ x \\ y \\ z \end{bmatrix} = \begin{bmatrix} -16 \\ 20 \\ -4 \\ -10 \end{bmatrix}$$

The first two screens below show the matrices being defined, and the third screen displays the solution.

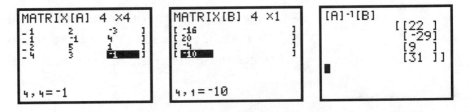

For Question 4, solve the matrix.

$$\begin{bmatrix} 1 & 1 & 1 & 1 & 1 & 1 \\ 2 & 3 & -6 & 4 & -1 & 1 \\ 5 & 4 & 3 & -1 & 5 & -2 \\ 2 & -3 & 8 & -6 & 1 & 4 \\ 6 & 2 & 7 & -5 & -3 & -2 \\ -5 & 8 & -5 & 3 & -9 & 4 \end{bmatrix} \begin{bmatrix} a \\ b \\ c \\ d \\ e \\ f \end{bmatrix} = \begin{bmatrix} 30 \\ 8 \\ 34 \\ 38 \\ -42 \\ -18 \end{bmatrix}$$

Again, the first two screens show matrices being defined, and the third screen displays the solution.

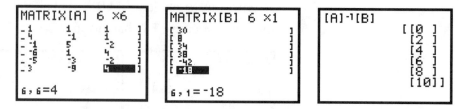

Students may encounter some difficulties while working on this activity. They must recognize that when variables have no coefficient written, it is equivalent to a coefficient of 1, so a **1** should be placed in the matrix. Remind students also that if a variable is omitted in a particular equation, they will need to enter a "0" in the matrix. Furthermore, when subtraction is used in one of the linear equations instead of addition, they must translate that to be equivalent to adding the opposite. Thus, the opposite of the coefficient must appear in the coefficient matrix. Finally, after inverting a matrix, a calculator may display some very small number, such as $2 \cdot 10^{-12}$. If this occurs, it is not due to student error. Rather than tell students that the actual value is 0, use it as an opportunity to ask if a number of this magnitude makes sense given the original problem.

Day 36

Students must rely completely on the ability of their graphing calculators to invert matrices to solve the unit problem. Thus, you can expect to do some "calculator debugging" in the next couple of days.

As mentioned previously, expect the calculator to occasionally report very small numbers, such as $2 \cdot 10^{-12}$, when the actual value is 0. Also, because the constraints have coefficients of 0 and 1 only, students must carefully organize their data entry into the calculator's matrix editor. The example below shows the matrix equation to solve for the corner point of constraints I, II, III, VI, IV, and VIII (as numbered in the *Teacher's Guide* for *Meadows or Malls?*). The solution as found by the calculator is shown in the accompanying screen.

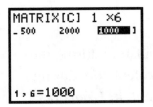

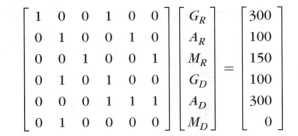

$$
\begin{bmatrix}
1 & 0 & 0 & 1 & 0 & 0 \\
0 & 1 & 0 & 0 & 1 & 0 \\
0 & 0 & 1 & 0 & 0 & 1 \\
0 & 1 & 0 & 1 & 0 & 0 \\
0 & 0 & 0 & 1 & 1 & 1 \\
0 & 1 & 0 & 0 & 0 & 0
\end{bmatrix}
\begin{bmatrix}
G_R \\ A_R \\ M_R \\ G_D \\ A_D \\ M_D
\end{bmatrix}
=
\begin{bmatrix}
300 \\ 100 \\ 150 \\ 100 \\ 300 \\ 0
\end{bmatrix}
$$

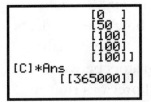

If the cost function coefficients are entered as a 1×6 row vector into **[C]**, the evaluation of **[C][A]$^{-1}$[B]** will figure the cost for this solution. First, enter the coefficients into **[C]**. Press MATRX , highlight the **EDIT** menu, and select **3: [C]**. Enter the coefficients (in the proper order) according to the cost expression $50G_R + 200A_R + 100M_R + 500G_D + 2000A_D + 1000M_D$.

Go back to the home screen by pressing 2nd [QUIT]. Then, enter **[C][A]$^{-1}$[B]**. Or, if the last answer is the result of finding **[A]$^{-1}$[B]**, simply enter **[C]*Ans**. Note that you must follow this order (**[C]*Ans**) because matrix multiplication is not commutative.

The screen shows that this allocation has a cost to the city of $365,000.

Day 38

In reflecting on the activities that helped them develop their understanding of matrices, students may want to include in their portfolios printouts of calculator screens or an entire matrix.

Use the TI-GRAPH LINK cable and software to connect the TI-82 or TI-83 to the computer either to print from the computer or to merge the data set into another file. (The TI-81 does not have linking capabilities.)

If students are aware they have this option, they may also want to incorporate pictures of the calculator screen or other data from the calculator into their write-up of the unit problem.

Day 39

Students should have access to graphing calculators during the in-class assessments. Comments about using calculators during individualized, in-class assessments can be found in *Fireworks: Day 12* in this guide.

Despite the possibility that *In-Class Assessment for "Meadows or Malls?"* may result in students discovering how other students have set up one of the matrices to solve one of the systems, this does not warrant clearing all work from calculators between classes. However, if you do wish to remove all previous student work, *Resetting Calculator Memory* in this guide provides detailed instructions on how to remove previous work from the TI calculator. Here is a summary of the keystrokes for clearing a roomful of calculators quickly. (*Warning:* This will erase *all* stored memory.)

TI-81: Press 2nd [RESET] 2

TI-82: Press 2nd [MEM] 3 2

TI-83: Press 2nd [MEM] 5 1 2

Appendix A

Supplemental Problems

Fitting a Plane becomes much less cumbersome once students have the ability to solve systems of linear equations using matrices and their TI graphing calculators. Students who continue to pursue the work from *Homework 27: Fitting Quadratics* usually end up with a very profound appreciation for the power of mathematics.

You may also challenge students to continue exploring the pattern from *Homework 27: Fitting Quadratics* by selecting four points and fitting a cubic equation. Again, the process is significantly less cumbersome with the power of matrices at their disposal.

Students set up matrices and evaluate matrix expressions in *Surfer's Shirts*. This can also serve as a reinforcement or practice in entering matrices and performing addition of matrices on the calculator. Students can also practice finding inverses on the calculator while investigating *When Can You Find an Inverse?*

If students pursue the extension activity *Determining the Determinant,* you may suggest that they also consult their calculator guidebook. They can learn how to have the calculator compute the determinant for a given matrix.

Calculator Guide for "Small World, Isn't It?"

The primary calculator topics in *Small World, Isn't It?* are slope, rate of change, and derivative in both numerical and graphical contexts. As students explore rate-of-change problems, the calculator's graphing capability allows them to formulate and test algebraic conjectures hand-in-hand with their graphic representations. Exponents, logarithms, and scientific notation will all play a part in the unit without requiring new calculator skills.

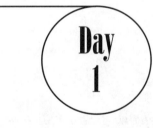

Day 1

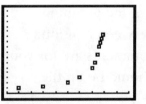

As students begin their initial work with the unit problem, *Small World, Isn't It?*, they may reach for their graphing calculators to plot the data pairs. This may be a great way for some students to begin to investigate patterns in this data set, even if they have little success. As directed in the activity, they should make note of any difficulties they encounter. Consult *Plotting Points* in *TI Calculator Basics* in this guide for a brief introduction to plotting points on the graphing calculator.

This unit problem involves very large numbers. Thus, students will be challenged throughout the unit to keep track of these numbers and to correctly read scientific notation on the graphing

calculator. They have studied scientific notation in the Year 2 unit *All About Alice,* so these ideas should be familiar to them.

Note the list of data illustrated on the screen, especially the entries in L2 for 1750 and 1850. This type of difference is usually sufficient to remind students about the advantages of scientific notation.

The possible ways to use the calculator are similar to those from Day 1. The same issues about plotting points and scientific notation may come up during work on either *Homework 1: How Many of Us Can Fit?* or *How Many More People?* You may wish to refer to Day 1 comments.

During the discussion of *Homework 3: Story Sketches,* you may find it helpful to employ certain capabilities of the graphing calculator while discussing the differences between continuous, discrete, and step functions. The following comments are for your reference; the focus of the day's discussion should be on the properties of straight-line graphs.

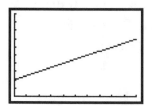

Some students are likely to draw a continuous graph as shown here for Tyler's accumulated savings. This is done simply by entering **.5x + 2** in the Y= editor and setting the appropriate viewing window.

A discrete graph can *occasionally* be modeled well on the graphing calculator. The rule for Tyler will not. (You will usually have better luck with discrete-looking graphs when the *x*-coefficient is larger, such as values of 3 or more.)

To see if a discrete graph will appear on the calculator, enter the function in the Y= editor. In this example, use the espression 3*x*. Then press MODE, highlight **Dot** instead of **Connected**, press ZOOM, and select **6:ZStandard**. The graph will appear, but tracing will show that the calculator has plotted every *x*-value in increments of approximately 0.21. Change this by pressing ZOOM, highlighting **8:ZInteger**, and pressing ENTER to return to the graphing screen, and pressing ENTER again. Then press TRACE. Tracing will show *x*-values in increments of 1. This method may not work consistently in the way you wish, but it should be helpful during classroom discussions.

Tyler's accumulated savings may be best described as a step function, and you can model step functions on the TI calculator. The command **int(** is the greatest integer function and will return the largest integer less than or equal to the value inside the parentheses. (The greatest integer function and its standard notation are introduced formally in IMP Year 4.)

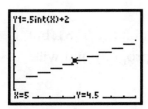

Enter **.5int(X)+2** in the Y= editor. Find **int** by pressing MATH, highlighting **NUM**, highlighting **5:int(**, and pressing ENTER. (For the TI-82 and TI-81, select **4:int**, and enclose the *x*-variable in parentheses.) Leave the calculator graphing mode set to **Dot** instead of **Connected**. Set an appropriate window viewing and then press GRAPH.

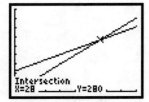

The activity *What a Mess!* is conducive to using the graphing calculator. Students should recognize that they want the radius of the oil slick to be equal to the radius of the clean-water circle. They can set up equations for the two radii, being careful to use the same meaning for *t* in the two equations. (For instance, if they use $t = 0$ to represent the time when the cleanup began, the equations would be equivalent to $r = 112 + 6t$ and $r = 10t$.) Students can then use either the graphing capabilities or function tables on their calculators to solve this pair of equations. See *Solving Systems by Graphing* in the *Meadows or Malls?* section of this guide.

Day 10

During the discussion of *Homework 9: Points, Slopes, and Equations,* you might ask students to verify if a particular ordered pair fits the equation. Students can test the ordered pair on the graphing calculator by entering the equation into the $\boxed{Y=}$ editor. They may then check the graph or table to see if the point fits.

One other method available on the TI-82 and TI-83 is to perform substitution using function notation. If the expression $2 + 5(x-3)$ is entered for **Y₁**, you might simply enter **Y₁(3)** in the home screen to evaluate **Y₁** for an *x*-value of 3.

(To get **Y₁** on the TI-82, press $\boxed{\text{2nd}}$ [Y-VARS] and then select **1:Function**. On the TI-83, press $\boxed{\text{VARS}}$, highlight **Y-VARS**, and then select **1:Function**.)

Note: It is possible to enter the same notation on the TI-81, but the calculator will not interpret the notation properly and will return an incorrect answer.

Day 11

During the discussion of *Homework 10: Return of the Rescue,* students should graph the function $h(t) = 400 - 16t^2$. When introducing the term *secant line,* you may wish to demonstrate a line connecting two points on a graph using the TI calculator.

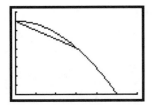

Once the graph is displayed on the calculator, press 2nd [QUIT] to return to the home screen. Next, press 2nd [DRAW] and select **2:Line(**. Complete the command by entering the coordinates of two points, each separated by commas, and pressing ENTER. The screen shown here used the command **Line(0,400,3,256)**.

Day 12

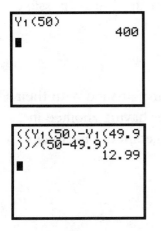

Students are likely to use the graphing calculator with *Photo Finish*. If students wish to substitute a particular value for *t* in the formula, once again they can use function notation on their TI-82 or TI-83. See Day 10 in this guide for details on how to do this.

Students might solve Question 2 by calculating the average speed during the last tenth of a second. The calculation illustrated in this screen uses the function $m(t) = 0.1t^2 + 3t$. On the TI-82 or TI-83, first enter this function as Y₁, and then duplicate what you see in this screen to calculate the average speed from $t = 49.9$ to $t = 50$. (Refer to Day 10 of this guide for instructions on how to enter Y₁ on the home screen for both the TI-82 and TI-83.)

The supplemental problem *Speedy's Speed by Algebra* generalizes this approach and can also be done in conjunction with the graphing calculator.

Day 13

Today's activities center around the graphing capabilities of the calculator. Students should be encouraged to use only the TRACE and ZOOM features in completing *ZOOOOOOOOM*.

```
Plot1 Plot2 Plot3
\Y1■.1X²+3X
\Y2=
\Y3=
\Y4=
\Y5=
\Y6=
\Y7=
```

Begin by entering Speedy's rule in the $\boxed{Y=}$ editor.

```
WINDOW
 Xmin=0
 Xmax=60
 Xscl=10
 Ymin=0
 Ymax=500
 Yscl=50
 Xres=1
```

Next, determine a reasonable window to view the entire 400-meter race. This screen shows one possibility.

Press $\boxed{GRAPH}$ to view the function graph. Then press $\boxed{TRACE}$ to move the cursor to a point near 400 meters (the end of the race).

```
Y1=.1X²+3X



X=49.787234  Y=397.23857
```

Now, press $\boxed{ZOOM}$ $\boxed{2}$ $\boxed{ENTER}$ $\boxed{ENTER}$ to zoom in on the graph. Try to get an ordered pair with a *y*-coordinate as close as possible (if not exactly) to 400 meters.

```
Y1=.1X²+3X



X=49.946809  Y=399.30879
```

Students can repeat this process until they are satisfied with their estimates. Using points found by tracing after having zoomed in on the graph should help to emphasize the geometric meanings of slope and rate of change.

Day 14

On this day, students consider the graph of a line tangent to a curve at some point and the way it relates to instantaneous rate of change.

The TI-82 and TI-83 will draw tangent lines. Brief details are included here for your information. It is neither expected nor recommended that students learn this calculator skill at this point in their investigation of instantaneous rates of change. However, you may find this helpful in demonstrating tangent lines, or possibly as an idea for an interested student to pursue later on.

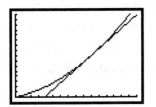

Graph the function in a reasonable viewing window. This example uses Speedy's function $m(t) = 0.1t^2 + 3t$.

Go to the home screen ($\boxed{\text{2nd}}$ $\boxed{\text{QUIT}}$). Enter the command **Tangent(Y₁,50)** and press $\boxed{\text{ENTER}}$. (To find **Tangent**, press $\boxed{\text{2nd}}$ $\boxed{\text{DRAW}}$.)

Day 15

By this point in the unit, students may have identified the feature on their calculator that determines the derivative of a function at a single point. Although this seems like a nice shortcut, you may wish to consider or discuss with your colleagues what risks might be involved if students move away from calculating average rates of change by hand to the more abstract process of allowing the calculator to do it for them. *Derivative at a Point* in this guide provides instructions on how to find derivatives automatically on the TI calculator. (The numerical derivative can be used in several ways, including in programs and in the $\boxed{\text{Y=}}$ editor.)

Question 3 of *Zooming Free-for-All* may elicit the idea that some graphs "peak" or come to a point. The absolute value function does just this.

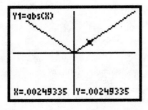

Have students graph the absolute value function by entering **abs(X)** in the $\boxed{\text{Y=}}$ editor. To do this on the TI-83, press $\boxed{\text{MATH}}$, highlight **NUM**, and press $\boxed{\text{ENTER}}$. (On the TI-82 and TI-81, press $\boxed{\text{2nd}}$ $\boxed{\text{ABS}}$.) It is a powerful learning moment for students when they zoom in repeatedly, thus allowing them to recognize that this function will never appear straight while all the others they had looked at do.

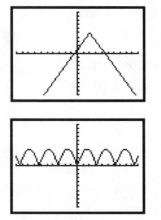

If students sketch an absolute value type of graph that is different from the graph of $y = $ abs (x), they may want to try drawing their graph on the calculator. You might start them off with a function defined by an expression like $-2\text{abs}(x - 2) + 5$, as shown here.

Some students may describe another type of function. Try starting them off with $4\text{abs}(\sin(x))$. Students will need to adjust the window settings to get the screen shown here.

Note: The TI graphing calculator's **nDeriv** function incorrectly shows that the absolute value function has a derivative equal to 0 at $x = 0$.

CALCULATOR INSTRUCTIONS

Derivative at a Point

The TI graphing calculator has a built-in command for estimating the numerical derivative of a function for a specific input value. The method approximates the derivative by calculating the slope of the secant line through a point slightly below and a point slightly above the given input value. This is very similar to zooming in on a graph very closely and tracing two points near the input value.

Calculating a Numerical Derivative at a Point

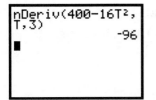

On the TI-82 and TI-83, begin in the home screen. Press MATH, highlight **8:nDeriv(**, and press ENTER. Next, enter the function you are working with. Follow this with a comma, the variable, another comma, and then the value of the variable at which you want to evaluate the derivative. For Question 1 from *Homework 14: Speeds, Rates, and Derivatives,* you would enter the information as in the screen shown here. If the function $Y = 400 - 16X^2$ is already in the Y= editor, then you can enter **nDeriv(Y₁,X,3)** instead of **nDeriv (400-16T²,T,3)** at the home screen.

On the TI-81, begin by storing the input value into **X** by pressing 3 STO▸ X|T ENTER. Then press MATH, highlight **8:NDeriv(**, and press ENTER. This will return you to the home screen, on which will be displayed **NDeriv(**. Enter **400-16X²,.001)** and press ENTER. If you have followed these instructions correctly, the TI-81 screen will display the solution of **-96**. Remember you can use any value in place of .001. If the function is already in the Y= editor, at the home screen press 3 STO▸ X|T ENTER. Call up **NDeriv(** and enter **Y₁,.001)**.

Day 19

If students have discovered the calculator's ability to determine the numerical derivative, they may be able to complete the derivative columns for *Slippery Slopes* rather quickly. As noted in the Day 15 discussion in this guide, there are advantages and disadvantages to having students do this.

If students do suggest a possible equation that expresses the derivative in terms of either *y* or *x*, encourage them to use their calculators to verify that the rule works. For example, students may enter the function into the Y= editor and then look at the table. The table should match approximately the values for derivatives they calculated.

Day 20

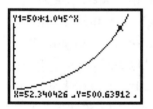

Some students may have solved Question 3 from *Homework 19: The Forgotten Account* by graphing and tracing the function defined by the expression $50 \cdot 1.045^x$.

Day 21

During discussions of *Slippery Slopes, Homework 20: How Does It Grow?*, and the "proportionality property" of exponential functions, it may be useful to be able to quickly refer to the

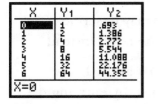

three-column tables students developed (only possible on the TI-82 and TI-83). This is not a skill that students should necessarily learn, but it may be helpful to you when facilitating this day's discussions.

If you enter 2^x for Y1 and $.693 \cdot 2^x$ for Y2 and then press [2nd] [TABLE], the calculator will display the three-column table as shown here.

Day 22

As students make presentations of *POW 10: Around King Arthur's Table,* you may decide that it is appropriate to introduce the concept and notation for the greatest integer function in relation to this day's discussion. This concept and notation were used previously only in the supplemental problem *Integers Only* in the Year 1 unit *The Overland Trail.* The notation will also be introduced in the Year 4 unit *The World of Functions.*

The TI graphing calculator has this as a built-in function. The greatest integer function can be found by pressing [MATH], highlighting **NUM**, and selecting **5:int** (select **4:int** on the TI-82 and TI-81). Try each of the examples illustrated in this screen.

Day 26

The exponential function through the points (0, 92,600) and (10, 380,000) can be found using the regression features of the TI calculator. However, in this activity, students should challenge themselves to find an exponential function algebraically.

To find the base for the exponential equation in Question 1, students must solve the equation $b^{10} = 4.1$ (or something equivalent). Some suggestions are offered in the *Teacher's Guide* for *Small World, Isn't It?*, but some students may describe something like "taking the square root, but the tenth instead."

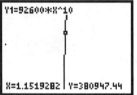

The TI-82 and TI-83 can do this. First, enter **10** in the home screen. Then press MATH, highlight **5:^x√**. Finish by entering **4.1** and pressing ENTER.

You can perform the equivalent operation on all three calculators by entering **4.1^(1/10)** and pressing ENTER.

Students may solve Questions 2 and 3 of *Homework 25: California and Exponents* by graphing, zooming in, and tracing the function defined by the equation $y = 92{,}600 \cdot x^{10}$.

Day 28

Students might solve pieces or all of *Homework 27: Comparing Derivatives,* Part I, using the numerical derivative feature of their graphing calculators. Encourage these students to consider the graphical perspective as well. Likely, they will have to for Part II.

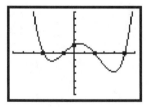

If students are determined to find an approximate rule for the function graphed in Part II, encourage them to pursue this using the calculator's regression capability or by extending the matrix algebra from *Homework 27: Fitting Quadratics,* in *Meadows or Malls?,* using some set of points on the graph (such as the five intercepts).

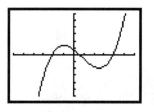

If students are able to generate a function that is similar to the graph from Part II, they can then have the calculator graph the numerical derivatives for this function as shown here. (See the section *Derivative at a Point* in this guide for help.) If any student investigates this, it is an exciting extension and is a mathematical "wow!" for classmates.

Day 29

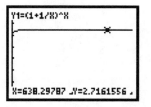

Students can investigate what happens as they use the calculator to compound more and more frequently. Enter the expression $\left(1 + \frac{1}{x}\right)^x$ into **Y1** and investigate the graph or a table of values. When entering this expression, be careful to follow the TI calculator's order of operations. Enter it as **(1+1/X)^X**. When students trace, they will recognize the *y*-coordinate as the special number *e*.

(If students have developed an equivalent expression, they should be encouraged to investigate it for large input values.)

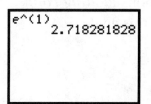

To get *e* directly on TI calculators, return to the home screen. Press [2nd] [e^x] and then enter 1 (enclosing it in parentheses).

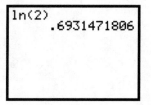

To determine the approximate value of ln(2) on the TI-83 calculator, enter the expression exactly as shown here by pressing [LN] [2] [)] [ENTER]. (On the TI-81 or TI-82, you need to enter the initial parenthesis yourself, or you can omit the parentheses entirely.)

Tweaking the Function does not have to be done in conjunction with the TI calculator's graphing capabilities, but students might identify the calculator as the appropriate tool to help them examine what their tweaking does. You might ask students, "How can you quickly compare graphs of two or three different functions?" Encourage students to graph two (or more) functions at a time in order to compare their differences.

Return to "Small World, Isn't It?" can be done using the graphing calculator. Students should plot all the data pairs and then test and compare the functions they create.

You might give students who are not yet comfortable with plotting points on the calculator the instructions *Plotting Points,* found in the *TI Calculator Basics* section of this guide.

Curve of Best Fit

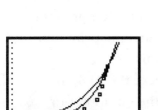

You probably would like to make adjustments to your original estimate of the exponential function so that it models more closely the changes in the world's population over the past several centuries.

Plot the world population data set and set a reasonable window range. Next, enter your first guess as Y1.

Improving Your Curve of Best Fit

Enter a new equation that is an improvement on your first try. If you like, leave your first guess in Y1 and put your new guess in Y2 so you can compare their graphs after pressing GRAPH. Continue improving on your best-fit exponential function until you are happy with it. But be patient, because this might require many tries.

Using Your Curve of Best Fit to Make a Prediction

You can use your curve of best fit and the calculator's TRACE feature to predict what year the earth's population will reach 1.6×10^{16} people. You may need to adjust the size of your window!

Note: The TRACE feature on the TI-82 and TI-83 moves the cursor along any graphed Y= functions or scatter plots. If you find you are tracing the wrong function or plots, press the up or down arrow key to move the cursor to the correct function.

Another option is to press 2nd [TABLE]. You can adjust the options in the 2nd [TBLSET] menu to aid your search.

Does your curve of best fit predict in what year the earth's population will be all squashed up? Do you think your prediction is reasonable? Do you think your exponential function is a reasonable model for the world's population?

Some students may have explored exponential regression on the TI calculator or asked about the meaning of best fit. They will do more work with best-fit curves and regression on the graphing calculator in the Year 4 unit *The World of Functions*. Students need not master calculator methods for determining best-fit lines during this unit.

Students may have done a great deal of work on their graphing calculator during this unit and may want to include printouts of calculator screens in their portfolios for this unit. Use the TI-GRAPH LINK cable and software to connect the TI-82 or TI-83 to the computer to either print from the computer or merge the data set into another file. (The TI-81 cannot be linked.)

Students should have access to graphing calculators during the in-class assessments. Comments about using calculators during individualized, in-class assessments can be found in *Fireworks: Day 12* in this guide.

Question 2a on the *In-Class Assessment* can be solved using the **nDeriv** command on the TI graphing calculator. You may consider or discuss with colleagues what understanding is being assessed with this question and what understanding is being shown in student responses. We recommend that you have students show how to find the given derivative without the **NDeriv** feature.

Appendix A

Supplemental Problems

Slope and Slant is an interesting extension problem that relates right-triangle trigonometry to the algebraic concept of slope. However, students may see no connection if their calculator is in radian mode! Press MODE and highlight **Degree**.

In *Speedy's Speed by Algebra,* if students are able to create an algebraic expression in terms of h for Speedy's average speed during the interval from $50 - h$ to 50 (see Question 2), they may recognize that the same technique can be used to calculate Speedy's average speed for other intervals of length h seconds. Students may wish to explore this further using the function-graphing and table capabilities of their calculators. You might get them started by asking, "Could your ideas be used in conjunction with your calculator's ability to graph or make tables from rules?" Students may take this idea in many different directions.

After doing *Proving the Tangent,* students may be curious about the graphing calculator's tangent features. Encourage them to use the TI calculator's guidebook to research this topic.

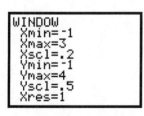

For your information, the following steps will yield the equation of a line tangent to a point on a curve on the TI-83. First, enter a function and reasonable window range. For example, if you want to find the derivative of the function $f(x) = 0.5x^2$, (from *Proving the Tangent*) at the point $(2, 2)$, you can use the window settings shown here.

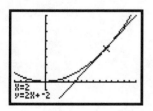

Then press GRAPH, which will take you to the graphing screen. Next, press 2nd [DRAW] and select **5:Tangent(**, which returns you to the graphing screen. Lastly, press 2 (for the value of x) and press ENTER. Displayed at the bottom of the screen is the equation of the line tangent to the curve at $x = 2$. (On the TI-82, after selecting **5:Tangent**, you must use the arrow keys to move the cursor to the point on the graph you want and press ENTER.

You can also use this method on the TI-83. The `Tangent` feature is not available on the TI-81.)

Use 2nd [DRAW] and `1:ClrDraw` to remove the tangent line.

Students with an interest in investing money (no pun intended) may wish to pursue *The Reality of Compounding.* Also, they may want to investigate the financial functions available on the TI-83.

Blackline Masters

Many of the graphs provided as blackline masters in the *Teacher's Guide* can be created on the graphing calculator if necessary. Specific instructions for most of the graphs are included in this guide's day-to-day discussion of *Small World, Isn't It?*

Calculator Guide for "Pennant Fever"

During the course of this unit, students will extend their understanding of the concepts of probability and of systematic counting methods. This unit emphasizes techniques for determining theoretical probability. You will also find the graphing calculator useful in these situations because it has a random number generator that can be used to simulate random events. This feature, combined with the calculator's programming capability, allows students to create and run simulations. Thus, they can run a large number of experiments to observe the likelihood of an event. These ideas were first explored in the Year 1 unit *The Game of Pig*. Also, as students explore ideas for modeling probability, the calculator's graphing capability will allow them to formulate and test algebraic conjectures hand-in-hand with their graphic representations.

Pennant Fever involves students in using the calculator to determine values for permutations and combinations.

The following discussion provides several opportunities to challenge students to explore and extend their mathematics and graphing calculator techniques.

Today's activities are intended to inspire various models to determine theoretical probabilities. But some students may begin *Choosing for Chores* by creating an experiment to simulate the situation. For example, they could place two purple tiles and three green tiles to represent the spoons in a paper bag. They could then select two tiles and see if they match. For this problem, the first tile drawn should not be put back in the bag.

The graphing calculator has a random number generator that can also simulate random events. The calculator must be set up to correctly simulate a situation, just as the paper bag was set up.

Random Numbers on the Calculator gives some basic tips on using this calculator feature. *Simulating Choosing for Chores* is a program that simulates the spoon situation. At this early stage in the unit, it may be a good idea to remind students about the simulations they programmed in *The Game of Pig* in Year 1. You can use *Simulating Choosing for Chores* with students who show an interest or as an extension to the classwork. Even better, challenge students to write their own programs to simulate the situation.

CALCULATOR INSTRUCTIONS

Random Numbers on the Calculator

Many probability problems involve the idea of picking something at random. In the simplest case, each possible result is equally likely.

Your calculator has a feature called a random number generator. You can use this to simulate probability experiments. You may recall working with this in the Year 1 unit *The Game of Pig*.

```
MATH NUM CPX PRB
1:rand
2:nPr
3:nCr
4:!
5:randInt(
6:randNorm(
7:randBin(
```

The **rand** command generates a random number between 0 and 1. Begin in the home screen, press MATH, highlight **PRB**, and select **rand**.

```
rand
      .2351261667
```

When the **rand** command appears in your home screen, press ENTER again. The calculator will display a decimal between 0 and 1 (it is unlikely to be the number shown here). Press ENTER repeatedly to generate more random numbers.

Simulating Rolling a Die

Random numbers can be used to simulate probability experiments. To model a six-sided die, let random numbers between 0 and $\frac{1}{6}$ (from 0 to 0.1666666666) represent rolling a 1, random numbers between $\frac{1}{6}$ and $\frac{2}{6}$ (from 0.1666666667 to 0.3333333333) represent rolling a 2, and so on.

Using Alternate Techniques

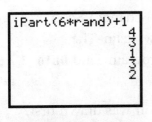

Reading all the decimals from the calculator can be tricky at times. Instead, enter **iPart(6*rand)+1** and press ENTER. (To find **iPart**, press MATH, highlight **NUM**, and select **iPart**.) Investigate what each part of this command does.

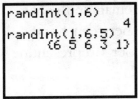

Another option on the TI-83 is the **randInt** command. Press ENTER, highlight **PRB**, and select **5:randInt(**. Complete the command with the range from which you wish to select integers. A third number defines how many random integers to generate.

CALCULATOR INSTRUCTIONS

Simulating Choosing for Chores

The activity *Choosing for Chores* creates a scenario in which Scott picks two spoons from a bag containing two purple and three green spoons. If the spoons he picks are the same color, he washes dishes. If they are a different color, he dries the dishes.

The instructions here describe a calculator program that simulates this situation. A calculator running this program can quickly produce many random outcomes of the game. The display here shows the outcomes of three simulations.

```
prgmCHORES
1 EACH
            Done
2 GREEN
            Done
2 PURPLE
            Done
```

To create the program, start a new program, give it a short and appropriate name such as **CHORES**, and enter the instructions from the column on the left. The column on the right explains the function of each programming instruction.

Instruction	Explanation
:0→G	Stores **0** in a cell labeled **G**. This cell will be increased by one for every green spoon drawn. Use STO▸ to create the → symbol.
:(iPart(5*rand)+1)→S	Chooses a random integer between 1 and 5 and stores this number in a cell labeled **S**. To find **iPart**, press MATH, highlight **NUM**, and select **iPart**.
:If S>2	If the condition in an "If" instruction is true, the calculator carries out the next instruction. If the condition is false, the calculator skips the next instruction. Find **If** in the PRGM **CTL** menu. Find **>** in the 2nd [TEST] menu.
:Goto 2	If the random number **S** was 3, 4, or 5 (a 60% chance), Scott draws a green spoon first and sets up to draw again. The simulation proceeds to label 2 later in the program. Find **Goto** in the PRGM **CTL** menu.
:(iPart(4*rand)+1)→S	The program gets to this line if a purple spoon was drawn first. Now, four spoons—one purple, three green—remain in the bag. Thus, the calculator chooses a random integer between 1 and 4 and stores this number in cell **S**, with the number 1 representing the purple spoon.

Continued on next page

CALCULATOR INSTRUCTIONS

:If S>1

:G+1→G

If the random number **S** was 2, 3, or 4, Scott drew a green spoon second. The cell **G** counts how many green spoons were drawn.

:Goto 9

The simulation proceeds to label 9 later in the program, where the calculater reports the results of the two spoons drawn.

:Lbl 2

Places a label for when a green spoon is selected first. Press PRGM and scroll down to select **Lbl**.

:G+1→G

Increases **G** by one to indicate a green spoon was drawn first.

:(iPart(4*rand)+1)→S

Now, four spoons remain in the bag—two of each color. Thus, the calculator chooses a random integer between 1 and 4 and stores this number in cell **S**, and the values 1 and 2 will represent the purple spoons.

:If S>2

:G+1→G

If the random number **S** was 3 or 4, Scott drew a green spoon second. The cell **G** counts how many green spoons were drawn.

:Goto 9

The simulation proceeds to label 9.

:Lbl 9

Places a label at the end of the simulation.

:If G=0

Find the = sign by pressing 2nd [TEST].

:Disp "2 PURPLE"

Displays **2 PURPLE** if **G** is 0. Find **Disp** in the PRGM I/O menu. Press ALPHA [␣] to enter the space.

:If G=1

:Disp "1 EACH"

Displays **1 EACH** if **G** is 1.

:If G=2

:Disp "2 GREEN"

Displays **2 GREEN** if **G** is 2.

Depending on what kind of calculator you use, it's possible to simplify this program using some special features. Also, you might want to improve the program by adding or changing the display lines. You could allow the user to input the number of green or purple spoons. It also may be helpful to have the program run repeatedly and then display the cumulative results.

Day 7

On this day, students may recall simulating random events using the random number generator on their TI calculator. Interested students can review *Random Numbers on the Calculator* in this guide.

Students need to design a simulation for the scenario in *POW 12: Let's Make a Deal*. The host must develop a random method for selecting the winning door. The command **iPart(3*rand)+1** will randomly select integers from 1 to 3. Press [ENTER] several times to get numbers like these shown here.

The supplemental problem *Programming a Deal* can be assigned to students interested in programming the calculator. Further comments and suggestions can be found in *Appendix A* in this section of the guide. You might have students start with *Simulating Choosing for Chores* in this guide, or you could challenge them to simulate that situation without the instructions.

Day 10

As mentioned in the *Teacher's Guide* for *Pennant Fever,* multiplying the fractions involved in the birthday problems on the TI calculator can become cumbersome. For example, this screen shows $\left(\frac{364}{365}\right)\left(\frac{363}{365}\right)\left(\frac{362}{365}\right)...\left(\frac{355}{365}\right)$. It's not easy to read!

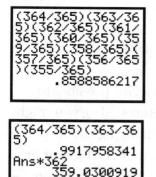

It is helpful to calculate each "additional person" from the previous results. For example, to get the probability of no match for four people, multiply the probability for three people by 362 and then divide that result by 365.

Day 12

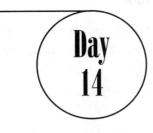

As students continue to work with probabilities, the question may arise about how many decimal places to round answers. You can help students avoid this issue by having them keep track of calculations using the last-answer (**ANS**) function of their calculator. In the screen shown here, the first line shows the probability that the Good Guys will win six of their seven games. In the second line, we are multiplying that result by the probability that the Bad Guys will win six of their seven games.

Day 14

To find the factorial for a number on the TI calculator, first enter the number on the home screen, for example, 6. Then press MATH, highlight **PRB**, and highlight **4:!** in the submenu. (On the TI-81, press MATH, and you will see **5:!** in the **MATH** menu.) Once this is highlighted, press ENTER to copy it to the home screen.

Day 16

The notations $_nP_r$ and $_nC_r$ are introduced today. It is important that students relate these notations to the types of counting problems they have been doing. Do not rush into showing students these functions on the calculators. However, students may find and learn to use them. Again, you must decide when it is appropriate to move beyond emphasizing the notation and the distinctions in the methods of counting.

POW 13: Fair Spoons could be considered an extension of the activity *Choosing for Chores*. With that in mind, students may wish to expand the program in *Simulating Choosing for Chores* for their work on the Problem of the Week.

This is the day to encourage students to learn how to use their TI calculator to do the computations to find an $_nP_r$ or $_nC_r$ value.

As suggested in the *Teacher's Guide,* students likely can learn how to do this on their own or with the help of the calculator guidebooks. *Combinatorics on the Calculator* provides a key-by-key approach that you may choose to give as a reference later on.

CALCULATOR INSTRUCTIONS

Combinatorics on the Calculator

You've probably been using your TI calculator to compute $_nP_r$ and $_nC_r$ values. But if you think having to key in all the multiplication or division is becoming too much work, you'll be happy to hear your calculator has a shortcut to compute permutations and combinations.

```
MATH NUM CPX PRB
1:rand
2:nPr
3:nCr
4:!
5:randInt(
6:randNorm(
7:randBin(
```

Press MATH and highlight the **PRB** menu. Behold the **nPr** and **nCr** commands.

```
Ans nCr ■
```

However, if you immediately select either **nPr** or **nCr**, **Ans nPr** or **Ans nCr** will be displayed in your home screen.

As you might have guessed, you must first enter the *n* value, where *n* represents the total number of objects. Then enter the **nPr** or **nCr** symbol as just described. Complete the command with the *r* value (the number of objects being selected).

```
7 nCr 2
              21
```

For instance, to compute the value of $_7C_2$ used in *Five for Seven,* begin on a clear line and enter **7**. Next, press MATH and highlight **PRB**. Then highlight **3:nCr**, and press ENTER. To complete the command, enter **2** and press ENTER to execute it.

Use a similar process to verify that 840 is the value of $_7P_4$ (used in Question 1 of *Homework 17: Who's on First?*).

Compare the values of $_5C_2$ and $_5P_2$. How are these values related? Is this relationship true for $_9C_2$ and $_9P_2$ also? What happens for larger values of *r*?

Day 20

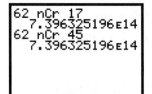

```
62 nCr 17
   7.396325196ε14
62 nCr 45
   7.396325196ε14
```

Students might be ready to develop the generalization that $_nC_r = {_nC_{n-r}}$. However, this topic can be delayed until Day 26. If you think it appropriate to do so today, ask students to make conjectures about what combinatorial coefficient is numerically equal to $_{62}C_{17}$. Students should test their conjecture using the calculator's **nCr** command. The size of this number may spark discussion.

Day 21

Students may be interested in further extending *POW 13: Fair Spoons* by investigating patterns among the possible combinations of spoons for which the probability of a match is exactly .5. They may have noticed patterns from the results they generated or the list created in class.

If a general formula is developed (an example is in the *Teacher's Guide*), it can be set equal to .5 to create an equation that describes all spoon combinations that fit the criterion. Encourage students to use this equation to write a calculator program or to use the calculator's function table to generate a list of spoon combinations.

Day 23

As students compare results to *Homework 22: Binomial Powers*, ask them how they can test to see if their expanded form of an expression is equivalent to the original expression. They may suggest looking at graphs or tables of the two expressions.

On the TI calculator (when dealing with only one variable), enter both functions in the Y= editor and then press either GRAPH or 2nd [TABLE]. (Tables are not available on the TI-81.)

Day 26

For your information, rows or "columns" of Pascal's triangle can be found using the TI-82 and TI-83 calculator's table function hand-in-hand with the **nCr** command. This might be a neat thing to bring up at the end of today's class by asking, "What if you used **nCr** in the Y= screen?"

In **Y₁**, enter **5 nCr X**. Press 2nd [TABLE].

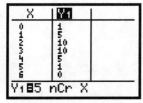

Or enter **X nCr 2** in **Y₁**. What do you think will happen when you press 2nd [TABLE]?

Homework 29: Graphing the Games asks students to draw bar graphs that show the probabilities of outcomes that are binomial distributions. The TI-82 and TI-83 have the ability to create bar graphs. *Graphing Probability Distributions* provides instructions about how to use these calculator feature. These instructions might serve as a good start to an extension activity.

CALCULATOR INSTRUCTIONS

Graphing Probability Distributions

In *Homework 29: Graphing the Games,* you created a bar graph showing the probabilities of the different possible outcomes for the Good Guy's Baseball Team. To create the bar graph by hand, you calculated the probability for each outcome and sketched the bars. The TI-82 and TI-83 can draw the bar graphs for you once you have the probabilities.

Begin by entering the number of possible wins, 0 through 7, in List 1 and the corresponding probabilities in List 2.

Next, press [2nd] [STAT PLOT] [ENTER] to adjust the options for **Plot1** as seen here. Press [2nd] [L1] or [L2] to enter **L1** or **L2**. Be sure to turn the plot on and highlight the bar graph option.

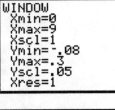

Next, press [WINDOW] to set the viewing window (or press [ZOOM] and select **ZoomStat**). Use the values shown here.

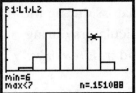

Finally, press [GRAPH].

Try adjusting these steps to draw the coin flip graph. Also, look in the table of contents of your calculator guidebook to learn more about the instructions and commands used here.

Once students have a sense of the general concept of a binomial distribution, you might want to show them how to find the binomial distribution probabilities on the calculator. (This cannot be done on the TI-81 or TI-82.) To find the probabilities for the Good Guys, begin in the home screen, then press 2nd [DISTR]. Highlight **0:binompdf(** and press ENTER. Press 7 (because they play seven games), press , and then press . 6 2 (because that is their probability of success), and press). If you now press ENTER, you get a list of the probabilities for each possible outcome. Press STO▶ 2nd [L2] ENTER to store the eight resulting probabilities to List 2.

Students should have access to graphing calculators during the in-class assessments. Comments about using calculators during individualized, in-class assessments can be found in *Fireworks: Day 12* in this guide.

Appendix A

Supplemental Problems

The problem *Programming a Deal* challenges students to write a program that would simulate the situation. The difficulty you face when students work on a complex program such as this is how to help them debug their programs. One helpful suggestion is to have students write out their codes and then follow them exactly themselves. Lengthy code can be printed out using the TI-GRAPH LINK software.

If programs are running the way students intend, it may make evaluating their programs less of a chore. If the results of many simulations on the calculators are near this situation's theoretical probabilities, their programs likely are set up well. Students should be able to describe why their programs accurately model the situation and use the correct probabilities.